POCKET GU

Shells

POCKET GUIDE TO

Shells

KENNETH WYE

Published by SILVERDALE BOOKS
An imprint of Bookmart Ltd
Registered number 2372865
Trading as Bookmart Ltd
Blaby Road
Wigston
Leicester LE18 4SE

© 2007 D&S Books Ltd

D&S Books Ltd
Kerswell,
Parkham Ash, Bideford
Devon, England
EX39 5PR

e-mail us at:-enquiries@d-sbooks.co.uk

This edition printed 2007

ISBN 10: 1-84509-467-0
ISBN 13: 9-781-84509-467-6

DS0170. Shells

Creative Director: Sarah King
Designer: Debbie Fisher & Co.

Material from this book previously appeared in
The Shell Handbook.

Font: Gill Sans

Printed in Thailand

1 3 5 7 9 10 8 6 4 2

contents

introduction

 Few of us can resist the fascination and beauty of natural objects. With the roar of rough seas or the gentle lapping of an incoming tide in our ear, who has not stooped to pick up at our feet that wonder of nature, the seashell, and admired its form, pattern and colour?

It is perhaps surprising that, considering our inextricable link with the sea, the great majority of people know little or nothing about seashells. And yet, how many of us have not combed through washed-up beach debris to find that elusive shell! Where did it come from? How was it formed and how did it grow?

Seashells, more scientifically known as marine molluscs (from the Latin mollis meaning soft), are the cast-off hard outer coverings of soft-bodied sea snails. They have been a source of fascination to us since the dawn of civilization. Shellfish have provided a valuable food-supply, and shells have long served as items of adornment, inspired our art, literature and architecture and even been used as objects of value, to indicate status and as currency.

Over the centuries, natural historians, conchologists (those who study shells), collectors and scientists have found in seashells an invaluable link with the natural world, enabling us to unlock some of the intricate and wonderful secrets of Creation.

Seashells are for the most part spectacular in appearance, displaying a host of shapes, forms, sculpture, patterns and colour. The diversity is almost endless – indeed, many species defy logic or comprehension, and some are so extraordinary that it is hard to believe that they occur naturally.

This handbook attempts merely to introduce a vast subject to the layman, giving the reader an insight into a few of the many thousands of existing species in our oceans. It is intended to help you to understand how they reproduce, grow, feed and where they live. It gives advice on self-collecting, purchasing, cleaning, forming and displaying a shell collection.

With our increasingly sophisticated lifestyles, aided by modern technology, we are forcing an ever-growing demand on our fragile world's natural resources. Alongside our desire to learn about and collect natural objects, it is essential not to lose sight of our mandate to manage and care for all our natural wonders. Seashells are by no means the least of them.

the classes of seashells

In order to make zoological classification easier, all living creatures are placed in major groups or 'phyla'. Seashells are placed in the Phylum Mollusca which is a vast group, second only to the insects in number (Phylum Arthropoda). Experts vary in their opinion but estimate in excess of 100,000 known species. However, new species are still being named today. The Phylum Mollusca includes marine, freshwater and land snails, sea slugs, squids and octopus.

All molluscs have an outer covering of tissue, or mantle, which, in many cases, secretes the fluid that builds the shell around its soft body. They have a foot, which is generally a means of locomotion, a visceral hump or mass that contains internal organs, and a gill which is primarily used for respiration – in some cases, greatly modified. Bivalve Molluscs (shells with two halves) do not possess a head and vary in other respects. To simplify this large group, the phylum is subdivided into six sections, known as classes.

CLASS GASTROPODA

Perhaps three-quarters of the world's molluscs are placed in this class, and about half of them are marine. These are the molluscs with one-piece, usually coiled, hard shells. The soft-bodied snails have a mantle, eyes, tentacles and a broad, flat foot. The vulnerable visceral mass is situated within the shell. Most Gastropods are highly mobile, active creatures. There are possibly 20,000 to 30,000 named species, which includes well-known shells such as Limpets, Periwinkles, Cowries, Murex, Volutes and Cones.

CLASS BIVALVIA

The outer shell of a Bivalve consists of two pieces, or valves. They are hinged together by means of a supple ligament. Strong interior muscles attached to both valves enable the shell to open and close the valves at will. The snails possess a large foot, a pair of siphons and a m antle. Most live sessile lives, a few 'crawl' and some, such as the Scallops, are highly active and move about in the water by 'flapping' their valves together in butterfly motion. There are approximately 10,000 species, and Oysters, Clams, Scallops and Mussels are included in this class.

CLASS CEPHALOPODA

Although a relatively small group, these are highly developed and mobile species. All are carnivorous and have large eyes, tentacles and suckers, and powerful beak-like mouths. These creatures differ greatly in their soft parts when compared to other molluscs. Nautilus have an exterior shell, octopus and squids possess no shell, and the Spirula shell is carried within its body. There are possibly less than 1,000 known species.

CLASS POLYPLACOPHORA

These strange creatures resemble woodlice, and are better known as Chitons or 'Coat of Mail Shells'.
They comprise eight separate plates held together by a tough leathery 'girdle'. They can have a broad or narrow foot, and microsensory organs, which are situated on the surfaces of the shell and girdle. There are perhaps 600 or more species.

CLASS SCAPHOPODA

The 'tusk' or 'tooth' shell is a small class numbering about 200–400 species.
They are the most primitive of all the shells, with a single, long, narrow, tubular shell that is open at both ends. The narrower, tapering end usually protrudes above the sand in which most species live. They do not possess a head, eyes or gills, but have a large foot and a radula.

CLASS MONOPLACOPHORA

These are the earliest-known molluscs, and fossil remains tell us that they existed as far back as the Devonian period, perhaps 400 million years ago. These long-thought-extinct shells were discovered alive in the 20th century in very deep water. They are a primitive limpet-like snail, with paired muscles and segmented body parts. They are extremely rare and can only be seen in scientific collections or museums.

the fossil record of shells

Molluscs have a permanent and undisputed link with the past. Fossil seashells are possibly the most numerous of all remains, due to the hard nature of their shells. Calcium carbonate preserves well, and most fossil shells and shell remnants have successfully withstood the long passage of time.

A few of our present-day species have links with earliest geological times. For example, the Nautilus has primitive ancestors dating back to the Cambrian period, and Slit Shells – a well-represented family nowadays – has fossil roots dating back to about the same time. This is an incredible feat of endurance and adaptability, particularly considering that these shells have remained in existence during huge, often drastic, global changes over vast periods of time, whereas many other early species died out long ago. Fossilized remains of Gastropods, Bivalves, Scaphopods and Cephalopods are well represented, but remains of Chitons, although first appearing in the Upper Cambrian period, are very rare. Monoplacophora also date back to Cambrian times.

Above top left: 'Recent' fossil shells from the Eocene Period.

Top right: Ammonite from the Cretaceous Period.

Bottom left: Halved Ammonite showing the internal structure, which is similar to that of the Nautilus.

Relatives of Nautilus – mainly straight-sided, non-coiled species – existed in earliest recorded times and a few others remained stable in number until the onset of the Mesozoic Era. It was at about this time that a great number of other species occurred, especially Volutes, Murex and Ceriths. During the Tertiary Era, in particular the Eocene period, the Gastropods became the most numerous of all molluscs – many families established then remaining, possibly with slight structural variations, until the present day.

Very few Bivalves were represented in early formations. A few with relatively primitive characteristics appeared in the Lower Palaeozoic Era, but otherwise little occurred until the late Devonian and early Carboniferous periods. Possibly due to prevailing swampy conditions at this time, new Bivalve species occurred, becoming more numerous and varied in the Mesozoic Era, including Scallops, Oysters and Brooch Clams (Trigonidae). In Tertiary times, Bivalves became abundant – species such as Bittersweet Clams, Razor Shells, Jewel Boxes (Chamidae) and Mussels, to name but a few.

Scaphopods (Tusk Shells) possibly appeared in the Mid Devonian period and have changed little from those times to the present.

Although molluscan fossil links are obvious in most instances (with regard to shape, form, etc) and many species have changed little if at all, there are a vast array of recorded fossil shells with most bizarre forms, that have long since died out. These comprise shells like Caprina, Spinigera, and the early long-spined forms of the Pelican's Feet shells (Tessarolax and Anchura) – all affording an intriguing study themselves!

Top: Ammonite section from the Jurassic Period.

Bottom: Jurassic ammonite from Yorkshire, UK.

the biology of seashells

GASTROPODA (GASTROPODS)

Members of this large and variable class live in virtually every marine environment. Purple Sea Snails (Janthinidae) live on the surface of the oceans (Pelagic), far from land. Below them, in the upper reaches of all seas, live the Sea Butterflies (Pteropods), many being shell-less, and a food source for whales. Rare and obscure species inhabit the dark, cold abyssal depths, but by far the most colourful, attractive and diverse of the Gastropods dwell in varying substrates in shallow waters close to land, where marine life can be found in great variety and abundance.

Most shallow-water shells do not enjoy direct or strong sunlight, concealing themselves under rocks, corals, in sand or mud, in crevices or caves in or under reefs, only venturing out at nightfall and becoming active.

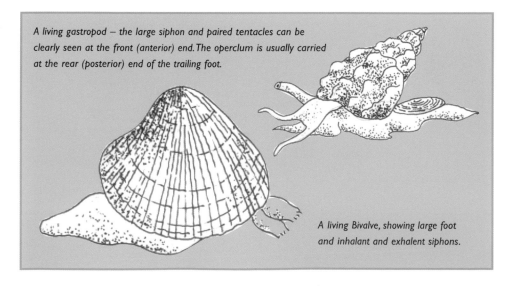

A living gastropod – the large siphon and paired tentacles can be clearly seen at the front (anterior) end. The operclum is usually carried at the rear (posterior) end of the trailing foot.

A living Bivalve, showing large foot and inhalant and exhalent siphons.

REPRODUCTION

The majority of species are of separate sex, although a few snails possess both male and female organs. Slipper Shells (Crepidulidae) start life as males and develop female characteristics as they mature. Following fertilization, most female snails lay their eggs in cases or capsules. These are of great diversity and form, each species having its own peculiar egg containers. They are released in the water to float freely or find anchorage to rocks or corals.

Cowrie shells actually brood over their young and protect their egg masses. After hatching, the young snails attain the so-called veliger (free-swimming) stage and many sink to the sea floor to commence a thin, fragile shell growth, while others, such as species of Tritons (Ranellidae), are borne along by ocean currents to far and wide locations.

Above left: Textile Cone (Conus textile Linne) is a species with vivid colouration and pattern.

Above right: Spotted Slipper Limpet Crepidula maculosa courad.

GROWTH

The hard outer shell of molluscs is made by a secretion of a substance called conchiolin, and is produced in the outer skin, or mantle. Once formed, the shell material basically consists of calcium carbonate.

Pattern, colour, structure and any sculpturing on the shell's surface are laid down in layers as the shell building continues from the mantle's secretion.

On the surface of many shells, you will find a skin-like coating of fine to coarse, scaly or hair-like material called periostracum, which usually totally hides any colour or pattern.

Little is known as to why most shells have particular patterns or colours, and, in many instances, the shell's spines or ribs have a purpose, but, generally, all that can be said is that both environment and diet have a bearing on the form a shell grows.

The growing period is often intermittent, with stages for rest. These stages can be clearly seen in the varices of Murex shells, and can often bear long and decorative ornamentation. Shells can have precarious lives and are frequently preyed upon, often by other molluscs, and

sometimes the shell can be damaged, either in the form of holes, cracks or chips. If this occurs, the snail can repair its own shells by growing on or over defects, usually repeating the characteristic pattern or colour of its species. Such repairs are known as 'growth scars' or 'healed breaks'. Many collectors prefer their specimens to be as near perfect as possible, as scars can affect the value of a shell, but most accept that these are natural occurrences and view them with interest.

In the early veliger stage, the body of the snail undergoes a kind of twisting process, called torsion, which re-orientates some organs into different positions within the visceral mass, often within the more tightly coiled rear part of the body, away from the aperture of the shell. The Gastropods are all spirally orientated and have included countless variations on this theme in the forms of their shells.

FEEDING

The more highly developed Gastropods, such as the Cone and Turrid Shells, are carnivorous and will eat other shells. Primitive snails are mainly herbivores, feeding on algae and other minute, suspended vegetable matter (Limpets and Top Shells). A third group of molluscs are both herbivore and carnivore, e.g. the Helmets and Conch.

The majority of Gastropods carry a retractable organ called the radula (made of chitin) which bears rows of rasp-like 'teeth' that enable it to tear at vegetable or plant matter or flesh. As these 'teeth' wear, new ones continually replace them.

Because many species are very similar both in shell and animal appearance, the radula is often a reliable indication of any differences between species and can be used in identification purposes when viewed under the microscope.

Predators, such as the Moonsnails, are able, by means of an adapted radula, to bore neat circular holes through the shells of their prey – hence many shells found washed up on beaches bear such holes.

The radula of the Cone Shells is further adapted, being able to eject a miniature 'dart' or 'harpoon' which is connected to a ducted venom gland. The radula 'teeth' are barbed and hollow, and, when confronting its prey, the Cone snail shoots a single, highly toxic 'dart' into an unfortunate creature, quickly paralysing it, after which the Cone proceeds to feed. Cone stings from the 'darts' of some species have been known to cause paralysis or even death to humans.

RESPIRATION

Gastropods possess gills over which water currents pass and oxygen is extracted – waste gasses being dissolved. In a relatively small number of species, respiration can take place in and through the mantle. The majority of Gastropods possess a trunk-like siphon, which extrudes from the anterior end of the snail, through which water is passed to the gills.

GENERAL ANATOMY

The heads of the snails (such as the Conch) are generally well developed and are made up of one or two pairs of tentacles, which often carry highly developed eyes that are able to perceive shape, light or darkness.

The strong and muscular foot is its main method of movement, and, in many species, a structure known as an operculum is grown onto the rear of the foot and serves as a kind of 'doorway', which closes off the aperture when the snail retreats into its shell, for example, if the snail is disturbed. These operculae can be thick or thin, can be described as calcareous, corneus or horny and are often ornamented and colourful.

In the cases of Conch or Carrier shells, the operculum is an aid to movement and is sometimes used as a weapon – as with the 'Fighting Conch'. Most Cone shells have minute operculae. They are virtually useless and are known as degenerate.

In Cowries, the mantle is often drawn over the entire shell, both sides meeting along the top of its dorsum, axially, resulting in many species portraying a clear dorsal line in the pattern, as in the Eglantine Cowrie. A more precise means of identification in Cowries are the small tubercules (or papillae) protruding from the mantle – each species having its own peculiar form and design.

Gastropods have a heart, arteries and blood sinuses. The nervous system is restricted to simple 'touch organs'. They are situated on the mantle surface, foot and tentacles.

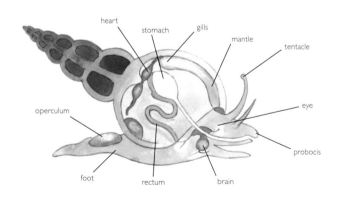

heart
stomach
gills
mantle
tentacle
operculum
eye
foot
rectum
brain
probocis

Above: A simplified diagram showing the basic internal organs of a Gastropod

BIVALVIA (BIVALVES)

Bivalve shells comprise two halves and, like Gastropods, are constructed in layers laid down by the mantle. The ligament, a rubbery connection piece, joins one valve to the other. In the proximity of the ligament is a hinge structure, often with interlocking 'teeth', which can be either simply formed or somewhat complex. Identification, classification and grouping of Bivalves are often done by means of these hinge structures.

Shapes of Bivalves vary considerably – being compressed, inflated, convex, rounded or ovate, elliptical or wedge-shaped. Valves are usually symmetrical and close together in a perfect fit, shutting off the inner or mantle cavity. The valves are said to be equal when both pieces are identical in shape and size.

Some species have gaping valves, usually to the rear, as in species of Giant Clams and Razor Shells, while others overlap, as in some species of Scallops. Other species have deep, convex upper valves and more or less flattened lower valves, as in some Scallops, Thorny and True Oysters.

REPRODUCTION AND GROWTH

The majority of Bivalve species have separate sexes and the reproduction cycle is relatively simple. In general, sperm and eggs are shed into the water, where they meet and fertilize. After hatching, the veligers slowly sink and settle on the substrate and start to grow their shells.

Growth generally commences on the dorsal side at the umbo, the area more or less adjacent to the ligament. Here, the internal 'teeth' develop forming in grooves on the opposite valve. When fully developed, they can vary considerably in both form and size. The inner faces of Bivalves are often smooth and porcellaneous or they may be pearly, as in the Pearl Oysters.

Muscle 'scars' are evident on the inner valves, and pallial or mantle lines run ventrally and roughly parallel to the edge of the shell. On the exterior, the shells can be smooth, sculptured or rough, as in the Oysters, and most display signs of growth in concentric rings spreading from the umbo. Many also have radial ribs, ridges or cords that often bear spines or nodules. Many species are highly coloured and patterned, while others are somewhat drab looking. Many Bivalves grow a periostracum.

Above: Brown-wing Oyster (Pteria brevialata Dunker) showing nacreous interior.

THE BIVALVE BODY

The soft parts are enclosed on both sides by two mantle lobes – these also secrete the shell-making material.

Although some species of Scallop and Thorny Oyster possess types of light-sensitive 'eyes' around the mantle margins, Bivalves do not possess a head or radula. They all have digestive organs, a heart and circulatory system.

Situated within the mantle cavity are the gills, which act as food filters for suspended micro-organisms and plankton and draw in the particles on the respiratory current by beating hair-like cilia in the cavity. At the posterior, part of the mantle of most Bivalves protrudes in two tubes, called siphons, one for inhaling the other for exhaling water. These siphons can be withdrawn within the shell prior to closure. Food enters firstly via the inhalant siphon and is then filtered by the gills and finally reaches the mouth.

Generally, if the siphon is long, the species lives in deeper substrate, often reaching twice the length of the actual shell.

The gills have little to do with respiration – the shell absorbs oxygen by way of the mantle. Waste material is carried away via the exhalant siphon.

Strong adductor muscles are used to close the valves, many species having two of these. Muscle impression scars are noticeable on the inner walls of the valves, and are often an invaluable aid in identification of the species. The supple ligament, found close to the umbone, has the opposite effect to the muscles; it tends to force the shells apart. The opposing forces enable the shell to open and close at will.

The variably shaped foot can be used for burrowing, creeping or attaching the shell to substrate and rock by means of byssus threads. In free-swimming and sessile species, the size of the foot is much reduced. The shape can be described as tongue, axe, or worm-like.

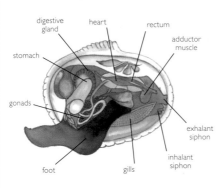

digestive gland — heart — rectum — adductor muscle — stomach — gonads — foot — gills — exhalant siphon — inhalant siphon

Above: The basic internal organs of a typical Bivalve

MOVEMENT

Although Bivalves are thought to be sedentary creatures, many species are highly active and live in diverse environments from inter-tidal zones to very deep water at depths of up to 10 kilometres (6 miles)!

The more immature or primitive species, such as the Bittersweet Clams and Ark Shells, move slowly over substrate but the majority use the foot to burrow in mud or sand. Mussels and Pen Shells are sessile creatures and live permanently attached to coral, rock or substrate by means of a fine filament-like thread known as byssus, made in the pedal gland. Some species, like the Piddocks and Angel Wings are capable of boring through and live inside wood pilings and even soft rock!

Free-swimming shells, such as Razor Shells, force water held within the shell through a jet at the rear edge. Scallops and File Clams are highly mobile and move through the water by clapping their valves together like bellows, again forcing water rearwards.

CEPHALOPODA (NAUTILUS SHELLS)

A varied class containing both Octopus and Squids, as well as the Nautilus and Paper Nautilus shells with which we are primarily concerned here. Most other species within this group are creatures without shells and are usually of little interest to the collector, apart from Spirula, which houses its shell internally.

In general, most sexes are separate, but unlike others molluscs, there is no free-swimming veliger stage – the embryo emerges fully developed, albeit small, from its egg.

Both head and foot are united and they have gills and highly developed sensory organs. All species of this class are carnivorous, and possess long, suckered tentacles, which are used to seize their prey. They tear at their food with a powerful, parrot-like beak.

The well-known Chambered Nautilus has a large single-coiled shell. Internally, there are sealed chambers or divisions, which are arranged in a perfect spiral, each being larger than the preceding one.

Left: Rough File Clam (Lima lima vulgari's Link). Right: Chambered Nautilus (Nautilus pompilius Linne).

Each chamber is interconnected via a thin tube known as the siphuncle, through which a nitrogenous gas is passed. This is required by the shell to create buoyancy for mobility. The animal itself occupies the largest, open chamber.

Nautilus occupy deep tropical seas, rarely coming to the surface. They were once thought to be the only survivors of the primitive fossil Ammonites, but recent study has shown that they are highly sophisticated and advanced shells which are well adapted to their own very peculiar lifestyle.

The Paper Nautilus shells are not shells in the true sense, but are protective egg cases of a female Octopus-like creature. Membranous 'arms' of the animal actually form the receptacle into which the fertilized eggs are placed, and these cases are set free on the surface of the sea prior to hatching.

SCAPHOPODA
(TUSK SHELLS)

These molluscs are unique, with hollow tube-like tapering shells. These primitive shells spend their lives buried in sand where the narrow, posterior end projects just above the surface. The foot is found at the opposite end and can be utilized to draw the mullusc deeper into the substrate. They have a large radula, but no eyes.

No true gills are present, but Scaphopoda breathe by inhaling water over the folds of the modified tube-like mantle lining.

Unlike other molluscs, food is not extracted from water currents. Instead the animal uses a kind of adhesive at the ends of its long tentacles, situated at the buried anterior end, where it grabs minute organisms found in the substrate.

Sexes are separate. The shell embryo consists of two tiny valves, which fuse together to form the long shell that is made by the mantle as it grows.

Above: Boar's Tusk Shell (Dentalium aprinum Linne).

Right: Neopilina galathaea, showing upper and lower view.

POLYPLACOPHORA (CHITON SHELLS)

Well known as Chitons or Coat of Mail Shells, these fairly primitive molluscs form a group which is the only class within the Phylum Mollusca to have flexible shells. The shell comprises eight segmented plates held together by a leathery girdle. The shell is able to coil itself up when disturbed or attacked. It has a powerful foot and can attach itself to its normal rocky habitat with great strength and is very difficult to remove once anchored.

The gills, sexual and excretory organs are situated within the mantle. Some species have primitive 'eyes' and tactile organs, which are found, on the exposed areas of its plated shell. There are no siphons or tentacles. Breathing is done by lifting parts of its encircling girdle, where water is taken in and passed over the gills.

The Chitons feed on algae and other vegetable matter by tearing at it with the well-developed radula.

Some species have a veliger stage, but most hatchlings remain under the mother until they can fend for themselves.

Above: Amaurochiton glaucus Gray found in Australia and New Zealand.

MONOPLACOPHORA

Little was known about this ancient class until May 1952, when a Dutch vessel named Galathea, fishing off Costa Rica. brought up from the abyssal depths a 'living fossil' that had ancestors dating back to the Devonian Period (approximately 400 million years).

It was taken on muddy substrate at a depth of about 3,590 metres (11,778 feet) and resembled a circular flat limpet, with a small, thin, cap-like shell. This long-lost mollusc, an amazing and sensational find, was named Neopilina galathaea. About ten other species have since been discovered and named, including one from the Red Sea and another from Aden.

They have segmented soft parts, paired gills, a radula, mouth and excretory, but no visual organs.

Scientific research continues on these extremely rare and primitive molluscs, and most known specimens are within museums or scientific institutions.

seashells habitats

As long as there is an adequate source of food available, shells can inhabit almost any environment in the seas. However, the majority of the worlds species, and certainly the most attractive and colourful, live in shallow waters. For the purposes of this handbook, we can divide the sea and seashore up into various zones.

Inter-tidal Zone

The area between high and low tide is sometimes referred to as the Littoral Zone. It is a vast area worldwide, supporting an equally vast number of molluscan species. This large area can be further divided. Sandy shores provide home for many species of Bivalves and burrowing shells. A rocky coastline provides excellent habitat for such families as Limpets, Top Shells, clinging Bivalves (such as Mussels and Oysters) and Chitons.

Mangrove swamps support yet other families such as some Ceriths and strangely formed oysters.

Sub-tidal or Shallow-water Zone

This includes the waters below the low-tide line, the unique coral reefs of the world, and the continental shelves.

Most marine molluscs live in this zone, below the low-tide line down to a depth of about 150 metres (492 feet), where relatively quiet and algae-rich waters support a rich fauna.

The coral reefs are home to thousands of species, especially the most highly coloured and attractive, the best-known being Cowries and Cones.

Abyssal Zone

Below 150 metres (492 feet) and down to the ocean floors is a lightless world where temperatures can be near to freezing. Here, mainly small and colourless shells – usually white or beige – exist, feeding on dead animals and pelagic plants that have sunk to the bottom. Both types of Gastropod, Bivalves and Cephalopods, have been found down to depths of about 5,000 metres (16,404 feet).

The Pelagic Zone

Perhaps 100 species inhabit the area just beneath or on the surface of many seas, and these are known to be Pelagic. Some float, others are attached to weed or hover in mid-water.

Right: Inter-tidal zones showing rocky and sandy coastlines

seashell structure

The hard outer covering of molluscs varies considerably depending on order, family and species. However, although the two main orders, Gastropoda and Bivalvia, have many theme variations, their anatomical forms can be described in general terms, as shown here. These scientific terms are essential when trying to identify shells – the majority of serious collector's books use the terms to describe the form, surface ornamentation, etc. They are particularly valuable when no picture is present.

BIVALVE SHELL

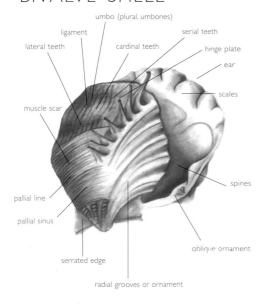

umbo (plural, umbones)
ligament
lateral teeth
serial teeth
cardinal teeth
hinge plate
ear
scales
muscle scar
pallial line
pallial sinus
spines
serrated edge
oblique ornament
radial grooves or ornament

GASTROPOD SHELL

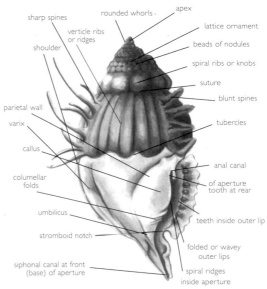

sharp spines
rounded whorls
apex
verticle ribs or ridges
lattice ornament
shoulder
beads of nodules
spiral ribs or knobs
suture
blunt spines
parietal wall
varix
tubercles
callus
anal canal
columellar folds
of aperture tooth at rear
umbilicus
teeth inside outer lip
stromboid notch
folded or wavey outer lips
siphonal canal at front (base) of aperture
spiral ridges inside aperture

the illustrated shell book

 With the upsurge of world exploration during the 17th and 18th centuries, naturalists and biologists increasingly returned from voyages of discovery with collections of natural objects, including seashells. Many of these shells formed the foundation collections for our national museums. It was during these times that the early illustrated books on seashells were produced.

Many rare and sought-after early works contained black and white engravings and later, beautifully coloured hand-painted illustrations and plates.

As research and study, alongside collecting, became intense, so biologists, students of conchology and wealthy amateur collectors began to insist on the correct 'tools' for their task, i.e., instructive, informative, and up-to-date, scientifically correct textbooks.

The early 'books', however, were basic and primitive and were probably more of a hindrance than a help.

The first practical work on conchology appeared between 1685 and 1692 as a series of over 1,000 unnumbered plates and was published by the physician Martin Lister in England. Although having no text or index, it was reasonably laid out in sensible sections. Comparable studies about this time were also produced by an Italian, Philippo Buonanni (1638–1725) and G.E. Rumphius (1627–1702), a Dutchman.

In 1758, the Swede, Carl Linnaeus, published the 10th edition of his Systema Naturae, which more or less brought together most of the literature and scattered information about shells available at that time.

The second half of the 18th century brought what collectors and conchologists wanted – illustrative works with text – and new books appeared, some by lesser-known authors such as Knorr (1705–61) and Martini (1729–78), both Germans. Martini's work brought together many previously unillustrated species and was a systematic and superior work in many ways. Regrettably, he died two years after the publication of his third volume, but a Dane, J.H. Chemnitz took over the work and added a further eight volumes up to 1795. The work was called Conchylien-Cabinet.

As time passed, more and more molluscan material became available – the bounty of Captain Cook's voyages from the South Seas for example – and as collecting increased in popularity, the books of the time became inadequate. More books were demanded, and, eventually, they came.

Between 1784 and 1787, Thomas Martin, an English shell dealer, enlisted the help and training of up to nine young boys as artists, the result of which was his Universal Conchologist, which, if for nothing else, won acclaim for the most beautiful illustrations. The haphazard naming of the species, however, was unacceptable in the light of the great work previously done by Linnaeus (see The Classification and Naming of Seashells pp 40–1) as a bi-nominal work.

In S.P. Dance's History of Shell Collecting, he describes the early 19th to 20th centuries as the 'golden age' or the 'abundant years', and while the greatest and most prestigious collections were being formed, the most notable literature concerning shells was being written and published. The hand-engraved or painted illustrations in some of these books were so precise and flawless in their representation that the sheer beauty of them remains unsurpassed to this day.

Further important titles appeared such as Reeves' & Sowerbys' Conchologia Iconica (1843–78) – a lifetime work consisting of 20 volumes (which nowadays can cost many thousands of pounds), Perry's Conchology (1811), Swainson's Exotic Conchology (1821–35) and the Sowerby Family's Thesaurus Conchylorum, to name but a few – all with very fine hand engravings.

Many shells depicted in early engravings appear to be sinistral (rare left-handed coiled shells) because printers frequently forgot to reverse the engraving when printing.

More books arrived on the scene – by Hanley (1819–99) and Woodward (1821–65), both Englishmen, and by Tryon (1838–88) and Pilsbry (1862–1957), both American.

It is interesting to note that many of the well-known shell book authors have described or have had shells bearing their own names. Pilsbry, in particular, to his credit, described or named several thousand.

There seemed to be a lull in producing shell books and collecting seashells in general during the late 19th and early 20th centuries, the world wars being attributing factors. With modern technological advances since the 1950s there has been an upsurge in shell book publication and colour reproduction has gone from strength to strength. Many currently available editions are superb, both in quality of illustration and text.

Not only are there now reprints and facsimile editions of the older works, but titles to cover virtually every major family, such as Cowries, Cones, Volutes and Olives. There are also several excellent worldwide guides (see Bibliography p240).

Limited circulation and high production costs make most specialist shell books somewhat expensive. Antique conchological works are mostly in the hands of societies, museums and a few privileged collectors and hardly ever become generally available.

the influence of seashells

Over the centuries, we have had an inseparable link with seashells, and many aspects of our culture and lifestyle have been, and continue to be, influenced by them. Our museums house and display large collections, both scientific and ethnological; we can identify shells in art, architecture, and religion. We eat them (or, at least, the creatures they contain), we wear them, we collect them, we have traded with them, and we use them as items of decoration, both for ourselves and in our homes.

FOOD

Since the earliest civilizations, we have relied on seashells to provide a major food source. They are relatively easy to harvest from shallow waters and, although not to everyone's taste, most are edible and many delicious!

Evidence of huge dumps of waste shells, or 'middens', have been found in many worldwide coastal areas dating back many thousands of years – one important early coastal site being the Klaises River Mouth Cave in South Africa. Species like Cockles, Mussels, Oysters and Limpets were found, along with other animal bones and waste material. Other substantial middens have been discovered in far-flung places like Japan, Western USA and Northern Europe.

As a ready food source, the Romans were amongst the earliest civilizations to farm molluscs, in particular Oysters, as well as the large edible land snail, Helix pomatia, more commonly known as the Roman snail.

The Victorians in Britain, popularised eating Cockles, Mussels and Whelks at public house venues. In Hawaii, boiled sea snails have long been a popular dish and in Japan, Tiger Cowrie (Cypraea tigris) roasted over hot coals is considered a delicacy. To this day, islanders of the Indo Pacific regularly eat seafood as part of their diet, and in the Philippines virtually every shell creature fished is consumed – even the toxic species – after the removal of the poisonous parts.

National dishes like Clam Chowder and Conch or Abalone steaks can be eaten in the USA, while in Europe we can indulge in the French delights of Moules Marinières, Coquilles St Jacques and Bouillabaisse, or the Italian Spaghetti alle vongole (Pasta with clams).

Above: The edible European Whelk (Buccinum undatum Linne) is a well-known food species.

ART AND ARCHITECTURE

Shells have long inspired art and artists, and alongside mankind's need to eat has been his drive to create beauty. Man first started working and using shells for artistic purposes some 30,000-40,000 years ago. Carved and worked shells for adornment and jewellery have been discovered in various early cultures in America, Africa and Europe. One of the early surviving shell art forms is a sculpted Triton Shell (Charonia) in alabaster dating from the Minoan culture of early Crete, possibly 3500BC. Shell form also featured in the ceramic art of many early American cultures such as the Aztecs and inhabitants of early Peru.

As time passed, seashell motifs, both accurate and fanciful appeared increasingly. The Scallop Shell, in particular, has proved extremely popular. The Scallop appeared carved in stone to decorate Roman coffin lids and marble tombs from Asia Minor, as well as niches and porticoes in palaces and in church doorways. Ancient Greek statuettes display scallops and they also occur in Roman mosaics. In modern times, The Shell Oil Company chose the Scallop as their now world-famous emblem.

Drawings of shells by Leonardo da Vinci depict beauty and form, and may well have inspired early designs for spiral staircases – in particular the famous -one at the Château de Blois in France.

Indeed the shell may have influenced some building design. It is credible that oriental pagodas were inspired by the many pagoda-like shell species, and it is alleged that the Japanese Wonder Shell (Thatcheria mirabilis) inspired Frank Lloyd Wright in his design of the Guggenheim Museum in New York.

Seashells occurred frequently in the paintings of the Dutch Masters of the 17th and 18th centuries. The Dutch had strong links with the Far East and the Indies and many shells were brought back to Europe from the old trade routes to supply an eager demand amongst not only collectors but also artists such as Rembrandt, Vander Ast and Stoskopff. Some Dutch and Flemish painters were commissioned to paint portraits of various individuals with their favourite shells alongside them!

(See also The Illustrated Shell Book – A Brief History pp 22–3)

JEWELLERY AND ADORNMENT

Early discoveries reveal shell beadwork and small-carved shells for personal adornment amongst early cultures in several continents.

Cowrie Shells have always been a popular personal adornment, and were widely worn by Roman women and given as wedding gifts. The famous Golden Cowrie (Cypraea aurantium) was worn as a pendant by chieftains on the islands of Vanaut and Fiji to signify rank.

As the interest in collecting continued to grow from the 17th to the 19th centuries, so also the fashion for shell jewellery and decor developed. Wonderful ornately worked chalices and goblets were fashioned with Nautilus shells cradled in supports of fine silver and gold, often encrusted with semi-precious stones and red corals.

Hair slides, combs, brooches and earrings appeared, made from shell material such as mother of pearl and other nacreous Oysters.

The Victorian craftsmen brought us shell-framed mirrors, mother of pearl calling-card cases, shell purses and scent bottles, and in Italy, we see the emergence of the very popular work of cameo carving (using Helmet shells – Cassidae).

In the 1970s and 1980s new and exciting designs of shell jewellery flooded the market. Not all was particularly tasteful, but some very good material was made in Taiwan and the Philippines from mother-of-pearl, Abalone and other shell material.

Today, a few individual innovative designers and craftsmen continue to supply a small but affluent clientele with both classic and abstract jewellery.

DECORATIVE ITEMS

A popular art form of the 19th century was the engraving of certain species of shell – especially those with contrasting colour below the surface.

Tiger Cowries (Cypraea tigris), and the Nautilus (Nautilus pompilius) have been engraved with the Lord's Prayer and other biblical passages, as well as various classical scenes and floral designs. There are many fine examples of such work in both private collections and folk and craft museums.

The art of shell collages has again become popular, resurrecting a well-known Victorian craze, where large and often over-ornate glass-domed 'floral' displays made from shells were painstakingly created by deft fingers.

Sailors' Valentines – collages of usually very small shells, beautifully arranged in wooden frames and under glass, which were purchased or often made by sailors returning home from long voyages, as gifts for their sweethearts – have now become popular and expensive collector's items. Several artists have in recent years created a revival in this exquisite shell art and pieces are commissioned or sold via eminent auction rooms, galleries, or at exhibitions at high prices.

The fashion industry is volatile, but the last decade or so has seen a continuance in seashell interest, not only in jewellery, but also as part of interior decor as a whole. Shell motifs and designs have widely appeared in both materials and decorative household articles and accessories like drapes and curtains, tiles and wallpapers.

RELIGION AND BELIEFS

The Scallop shell, and in particular Pecten jacobaeus, more commonly known as St James's Scallop (the Saint's emblem), was carried by Christian pilgrims – particularly in the Middle Ages – on their return from his shrine at Santiago de Compostella in Spain, as proof of their pilgrimage. The shells were sold within the town and, according to papal ruling, anyone caught selling the shells outside the town was excommunicated from the faith!

The Scallop also became the symbol of the Crusaders of the 12th and 13th centuries in their attempts to liberate Jerusalem. Families who participated in the Crusades displayed the shell on their coats of arms.

A greatly venerated shell, the Indian Chank (Turbinella pyrum) has been sacred to the Hindu god, Vishnu, in India, China and Tibet for thousands of years. Water poured from the shell is thought to be holy, and larger shells, made into trumpets, are still used at Vishnu wedding and funeral services. The extremely rare left-handed form of the Chank is highly treasured and often encrusted with gold and precious stones.

In early cultures, particularly those of Central and South America, shells that could produce sound by blowing, knocking or rattling, were believed to attract the attention of spirits or the gods.

Olive shells were associated with water or rain by some of the early Native American cultures.

Cowrie shells have long been considered good-luck fetishes. Many cultures in the Americas, Africa and tropical islands worldwide consider Cowries to be fertility symbols.

The Triton Trumpet shell (Charonia tritonis and other large Triton species) have been used in religious ceremonies by Shinto priests. On his South Pacific voyages Captain Cook remarked that the sound of the Triton trumpet shell usually signalled trouble because it called native warriors into battle!

CURRENCY AND TRADE

Although seashells should not be considered secure financial investments nowadays, for many thousands of years numerous species have been used as forms of money and in bartering and trading.

Cowrie shells, particularly, figure highly in currency, primarily Cypraea moneta and annulus. In times past, the use was widespread in Asia, Africa and most of the Indian Ocean and Malaysian islands.

These Cowries were abundant in these areas, in particular the Maldive Islands, which was one of the most prolific suppliers of Cowries. They were easy to collect and to transport (often strung into lengths), and large fortunes were made by early traders who brought them back from tropical islands to places like West Africa, where they were exchanged for semi-precious stones, palm oil and ivory. Prior to AD1000, Persian and Dutch traders shipped huge quantities of cowries to Africa in exchange for slaves and gold. By the 16th century, European traders (Portuguese, Dutch, English and French) began to trade in shells (See also Shells as Currency on p234).

Cowries even reached the Americas as early as Columbus's time, and early sites and excavations show that the native peoples had an association with shells as items of value.

Some tribes ground down Bivalve shell pieces, called Wampum, to use for trading. Clams, especially those with purple interiors, Tusk Shells, Olives and Abalones were pierced or drilled and strung on sinews and traded, as well as other varieties.

One of the most precious by-products of shells in times past was that of the endemic Mediterranean shells Murex trunculus and Murex brandaris. A gland in the mantle of Murex shells, in particular, produces a fluid, which, on exposure to sunlight, will turn purple.

Many thousands of shells were required to produce only a very small quantity of this fluid, which was used as a dye. Early Mediterranean cultures, particularly the Phoenicians, perfected this difficult and time-consuming industry. The dye became known as Tyrian purple because Tyre and Sidon became the main distribution centres. (See also Famous Shells p112)

The dye was extremely expensive and therefore only the wealthy and royalty could afford it. Both the Egyptian and Roman courts obtained the precious fluids for materials used by their kings, queens, emperors and others of high station.

Both the pre-Roman British and early South American cultures produced dyes from locally harvested shells.

conservation

We are becoming increasingly concerned about the havoc mankind is wreaking on our natural environment, and it is an unfortunate fact of life that as we become more sophisticated and modern technology advances, and as under-developed countries endeavour to crawl out of poverty and improve themselves, our natural world is suffering as a result.

The 20th century has seen an enormous growth in technological advances, in how we all work, how we enjoy our leisure time, and, as each nation finds its own feet in terms of prosperity, we seem to encroach increasingly on the habitats of the natural world. We are often careless, irresponsible and selfish, in our unending attempts to better ourselves, and our exploitation of the natural world and its wildlife, including shells is having disastrous results.

The most important threat to the seashell is the destruction of its habitat, and this occurs for a number of reasons. Pollution is the number-one killer – we dump vast quantities of sewage, rubbish and industrial waste into our oceans, particularly in proximity to populated land masses, where shallow-water marine life abounds. News of oil spillages and tanker disasters are commonplace.

It is possible that we are storing up future disasters by dumping nuclear waste in the depths of the seas – however far from land we dispose of it.

We have destroyed large areas of coral reefs – which support a mass of marine life – in the cause of new harbours and ports, airport landing sites, land reclamation and general re-development. Also, natural forces play their part in causing huge damage to reefs and shallow-water habitats due to cyclones, hurricanes and the like.

A great many species of shells are harvested from coral reefs and provide a significant income in developing countries, both in terms of food supply and sale of the by-product – shells. In many areas such as India, Malaysia and the Philippines, warm, shallow seas provide vast areas of ideal habitat where seashells thrive. Since perhaps the early 1960s, a steady growth in demand from these places for the marine curio, mother of pearl and fertilizer industries – all dependant on regular supplies – have seen many thousands of tonnes of shells exported annually to markets in America, Europe and the Far East and over-exploitation has in some areas become commonplace, resulting inevitably in local fishing bans.

However, as the world's populations increase, and ever-greater demands are placed on the seas for providing food, we see extensive over-fishing, not only of fish, but all seafood including seashells. Tough controls are surely called for if we are to sustain our natural marine resources for future generations.

In recent years, the Convention on International Trade in Endangered Species (CITES) was formed to prevent over-exploitation of both animals and plants. Over 100 countries are party to the convention and this is helping to control the taking, harvesting and fishing of numerous natural creatures which otherwise by now may have become extinct. The system is regrettably open to some fraudulent practice, but in general appears to work well. There are fortunately only a few seashells listed and controlled under CITES (meaning in general that currently most species are not under threat from over-harvesting and collecting, but prudence is necessary) and these are all species of the Clam family

Right: Giant Clam (Tridacna gigas Linne) has been overfished for many years, but is now tightly controlled.

(Tridacnidae), and Strombus gigas (Queen Conch). Clam shells are nowadays being farmed in some areas, notably Micronesia, Palau and the Marshall Islands as a long-term work to replenish stocks.

Marine nature reserves are now common and can be found in places like the USA (Florida), the Red Sea, Australia, the Maldives and the Seychelles all of whom impose stiff penalties for the removal of any form of marine life from their shores or waters. Other places restrict collecting to a few specimens, or to adult – and not immature shells – in particular species.

In underdeveloped countries where tropical shells are abundant, there is a great need to educate the natives to fish and harvest sensibly on a sustainable level to conserve stocks for the future. Controlled commercial farming on a large scale and the relatively new science of mariculture could here be key factors in the future.

There is little evidence to support the claim that shell collectors are responsible for depleting large numbers of mollusc species, but there is a need for all collectors and students of conchology to take the lead in having a responsible attitude and respect when collecting from the wild. This means to abide by all local collecting bans and, above all, in disturbing as little as possible the habitats in which shells are to be found. Corals on reefs should not be disturbed, and any rocks or slabs should be replaced as found. Do not over-collect and never take immature specimens which should be left to grow and breed. (If the snails of shells you fish are to be eaten, take local advice, or consult one of several books on the subject before indulging.)

Collectors ought to avoid destructive self-collecting methods. Buy, where possible, from dealers that respect not only the environmental import laws of their own country, but those of the country from which the shells originated. Taking a keen interest in shell collecting should surely foster a care and concern about our natural history and will benefit rather than destroy.

Below: Trumpet Triton (Charonia tritonis Linne). This species is now carefully monitored in the Philippines.

forming a collection

Serious shell collecting has been with us for hundreds of years. After the voyages of discovery in the 16th and 17th centuries, and later when scientific expeditions returned laden with natural objects, shells were particularly sought after for a variety of reasons.

In Europe, royalty, the wealthy and learned folk became fascinated by these wonders of nature and quickly amassed 'cabinets' and galleries of collections to show off to admiring friends. Some bought expensive shells for investment and status, others, such as naturalists and scientists, studied their beauty and form and tried to make some sense of the groups and families that existed and were available at that time. Others made lavish decorative objets d'art to adorn mansions and chateaux when holding extravagant functions.

Nowadays most places in the world are relatively easily accessible, and, with modern fishing and collecting methods, most known species are available to the collector either by self-collecting, purchasing or exchanging – even the once very rare species. No time has been better than the present to start a shell collection.

Amateurs and professionals alike collect shells – for the beauty of their various shapes and colours, to provide inspiration in art and photography, for home decoration, and for personal adornment. As with many collecting hobbies, some people find it becomes almost an obsession and spend large amounts of time, effort and money expanding their collection.

Because a shell collection requires space in which to house it, some collectors choose to specialize in collecting particular families or groups, or maybe even sizes of seashells. A general collection is fine to start with, but as home storing limitations arise, then some hard decisions have to be made! Few of us have the luxury of having a room at home that can be devoted to housing a collection! Also, serious study of many seashell families is restricted due to the immensity of the subject, so specialization becomes the obvious choice.

Cowries are by far the most popular group due to their relatively small sizes (the largest species is perhaps no larger than 15cm/6in), their shiny and colourful appearance, their relative ease of collection in the wild and the fact that many can be purchased at affordable prices. A modest or even large collection is easy to house in a small or medium-sized cabinet or showcase alongside a bookcase or in a corner of a room. Next in popularity come Cones, then Murex, Volutes, and so on.

Some people prefer to collect small and miniature species ('microshells') which rarely exceed 1cm (3/8in) at maturity, while others seek out freaks and abnormalities. As with all things natural, abnormal deviants do occur, and, although relatively uncommon, shells with growth defects, stunted or abnormally large growths, strange attachments or damage due to predatory attack or upheavals in lifestyle, are sources of fascination to many collectors.

Pollution and toxic deposits in seawater cause some molluscs to be discoloured or grow in freakish and bizarre manners. The Cowries of New Caledonia have developed lengthened and curved extremities, possibly due to chemical deposits in the seas around the islands. These Cowries, known as 'rostrate' specimens, are highly sought-after and can command very high prices. Some shells here also adopt a dark brown or near black colouration that bears little resemblance to the normal colour or pattern of the given species. These are known as 'niger' or 'melanistic' forms and are both rare and expensive.

Below: Draws of scientifically arranged Cowies form the basis of a superb collection.

SELF-COLLECTING

The most accessible area to find shells and start your collection is the beach or shoreline. You will undoubtedly find beach-worn specimens amongst the sand or pebbles, and, after storms or high wind-swept seas, 'fresh-dead' shells. Many collectors find these washed-up specimens quite acceptable.

Many live species that reside in the mud or under the sand are within reach with the aid of a spade or shovel, but always be aware of the movements of the tide as time can pass unnoticed when you are collecting. Also, remember to take suitable precautions against the sun's harmful rays and wear sensible head and body protection, particularly when in the tropics.

Rocky areas are an ideal hunting ground for many species well adapted to live in pools, under rocks and in cracks and crevices. Strong footwear is essential (plastic shoes are ideal). The same applies when collecting on coral reefs, where both corals and rocks can be razor sharp and cut your feet. Be aware of all marine creatures that could inflict stings or scratches, and be careful to avoid any sharp, spinose shells lurking just below the surface. As a minimal requirement, you will require strong plastic bags and a bucket for your finds, protective rubber gloves, a sharp knife and possibly forceps.

Any collecting in deeper water will initially require snorkelling equipment and a face mask. Areas not within walking, wading or swimming distance from the shore will necessitate the use of a small boat. Free-diving is useful, but is an art that requires stamina and a strong and competent swimming technique. Scuba diving is ever popular, and is the best method of gaining access to many uncommon and rare molluscs that inhabit deeper waters. Many package holidays offer diving tuition for beginners and can provide an excellent introduction into the wonders of the marine world, which would otherwise be out of reach for many of us.

If you are a poor swimmer, a simple dredge can be made and pulled along behind a small boat, and all kinds of interesting specimens can be brought up from the substrate. However, this method should not be used over corals, as damage can be done to the coral heads.

Wherever you choose to collect – on the beach or in the sea – always be aware of any local collecting restrictions, laws, or indeed bans, which could affect your collecting intentions. Remember, conchologists are mindful of the harm that could be done when collecting indiscriminately, and should take the lead when disturbing the natural environment. (See Conservation pp 29–32).

Right: *Collectors searching for shells on a rocky coastline at low tide.*

Most commercial fishing vessels bring up shells in their nets, and, regrettably, many are usually thrown over the side as unwanted. Lobster and crayfish fishers usually take deep-water species down to depths of over 200 metres (600 feet) and these, along with deep-sea trawlers and dredgers, are the best source for deep-water shells, as are those fishing specifically for shellfish on a commercial basis.

Many fishermen have long since realised that shells can be worth money and no longer discard them. With modern fishing methods, most of the world's known species are available, albeit at a price.

One of the most prolific of shell-producing areas is the Philippines, a country with over 7,000 islands ideally situated in the eastern tropics – a wonderful hunting ground for shellers. Most species collected there, numbering some thousands, are edible and are eaten by natives on all the islands. They use all manner of ways to collect shellfish. Whole families can be seen, often at nightfall, wading out in the warm, shallow waters to collect shells to eat for the following day. Most empty specimens are gathered and passed on to local dealers who make a good living selling, after much cleaning and preparation, to the rest of the world, a very useful by-product. Local markets in places like Cebu are heaving with seafood, and mounds of shells of many varieties can be seen on many stalls.

Many shells are often fished 'ex-pisce', i.e. taken from the stomachs of those fish that eat from the substrate, including molluscs. Many uncommon and rare species have been discovered when such fish have been gutted and cleaned out. The shells are usually in excellent condition, having already been well cleaned by strong gastric juices. At one time the very rare Cowrie, Cypraea fultoni was only collected by this means from the Mussel Cracker fish, off the coasts of South East Africa. Nowadays, it is rather more common, being fished by other methods in different localities.

CLEANING SHELLS

If you purchase shells from dealers, apart from periodic dusting or washing in warm soapy water, they should normally require no cleaning. Beach collected or dead shells can usually benefit from a wash and a light oiling (baby oil is ideal) to bring up any remaining colour. Use either a finger, or, with spinose shells, a soft brush. Any excess oil should be wiped away with a soft tissue. Some dull shells will even be brought back to life from a cycle in the dishwasher, providing any fragile species, such as Thorny Oysters, are carefully wedged in between other things to avoid movement. Live-taken shells have to be relieved of their inhabitants and killed off – especially if they are edible! Boiling the shells for a few minutes should do the trick (rather like cooking live Mussels or Clams), but avoid this method with shells like Cowries that have smooth shiny surfaces – cracking or blisters could occur on the surfaces.

Alternatively, immersing them in a 70 percent solution of alcohol for several days will suffice, or just leaving them to rot in fresh water will work but will take longer. There are numerous ways to extract the snail from the shell once dead. If cooked, this should prove easy, but stubborn body parts may require a period in the freezer, which causes the contents to shrink and fall away from the inner shell, allowing them to be removed using forceps or wire. In the tropics, it is common practice to put newly collected but dead shells in sand or soil enabling the insects to do their work and devour the occupants in a short period of time.

Many species possess an outer covering of flaky, fibrous or rough skin, known as the periostracum, which, in many instances, completely hides any pattern beneath. Most collectors prefer this to be removed. Place the shell in a 50 percent water/household bleach solution for up to 24 hours, after which the periostracum should be totally dissolved.

Other exterior debris often found on shells can cause removal problems – especially hard lime encrustations. A wire brush can be used with care on hardy species. Otherwise slow laborious chipping away of debris with pins, forceps or a sharp steel object may well do the trick, but, of course, great care is required on fragile shells.

I have always found that sturdy species with coarse ornamentation that are chalky or dull in appearance will respond to a very quick two-second dip in a mild solution of hydrochloric acid, known as 'Spirits of Salts' in the UK. Take care not to 'over dip' as holes will begin to appear! Some experts frown on this method, but I

have found it an excellent way to revive species such as Scallops, Thorny Oysters and Murex.

Often one is asked how to 'bring shells back to life' when they have been left outdoors for a number of years. Regrettably, the answer is that little that can be done – direct light can cause havoc with patterns or colour, and all shells should best be housed indoors to protect them from the elements and preserve their natural beauty.

Above: Philippino workers on the island of Cebu sort baskets of Pearlized Chambered Nautilus.
Right: Victorian multi-drawered collector's cabinet.

DISPLAY

Once you have collected and cleaned your shells, you will want to house or show them off to their full advantage. Any collection inevitably grows, and needs to be moved away from shelves and tabletops to a more suitable and permanent place of housing or display. Always remember that any natural light can be harmful and can eventually fade colours of any species that are not white or cream. Ideally, shells should be housed in multi-drawered cabinets, or, at the very least, on shelves or in glass display cabinets that can be covered by material or shielded by blinds from exterior light.

Most collectors prefer their shells to be housed in drawered units, which are sorted into families or by theme and displayed on a base of fabric such as felt, or placed on a bed of cotton wool in small plastic boxes.

Many argue that any collection without full or at least some basic collection data – name, where collected, habitat, date, etc – is worthless, and this is certainly true of a 'scientific' collection. Each shell should perhaps at least bear its name and locality on a small slip of paper within the shell or box – as collection numbers increase, it is easy to forget! Some collectors inscribe a small number inside each shell (with Indian Ink, or similar) and cross-reference this in a catalogue or on computer data. 'Full data' would entail keeping records of name, author and date, exact habitat of species where found, date collected and possibly name of diver/collector, etc.

However, if you decide to record details – even if you only collect for the sheer beauty of the shell – it is your decision how you organize your information. Any collection arranged tastefully or scientifically and kept in good order is a pleasure to behold.

PURCHASING SHELLS

You can buy shells from many different places – fishmongers, seaside souvenir shops, florists and, if you can find them, shell dealers.

New collectors will quickly learn to differentiate between poor-quality specimens and those termed specimen quality, which you will generally purchase from dealers. 'Commercial shells', i.e. those that, in general, are fished on a commercial, large-scale basis (perhaps for the seafood industry) are widely available, but the

Left: Purpose-made wall display cabinets are ideal for larger shells.

condition will often be poor due to rough handling, and the shells may be broken, cracked or chipped. The occasional 'find' will always be possible and you can often obtain very good shells cheaply. Because specialist shops nowadays are rapidly disappearing (due to excessive overheads) most dealers, both at home and abroad can be found on the Internet and will operate a mail order service. Another source is shell shows, usually arranged, on a regular basis, by shell clubs (see Contacts on p240 for a list of clubs and useful addresses). Shell shows allow you to select your shells personally, and, as a bonus, give you the opportunity to meet other collectors.

If you start buying from a dealer and you are pleased with the service get to know him; no doubt he will, in time, be keen to advise you of new arrivals and show you his rarer items. Should you have any doubts about a particular dealer ask other collectors.

Purchasing shells by mail order can, of course, be risky, and you will usually be asked to pay in advance until the dealer gets to know you and a mutual trust develops. Most are quite willing to exchange unsuitable shells, or offer a money-back refund. You will invariably be asked to pay postage – especially if ordering from abroad – for heavy species, this can be expensive.

Prices for shells vary considerably, for a variety of reasons. The comparative rarity will influence the price, as will the condition of the specimen, and, because each shell is unique, specimens with more attractive colours or unusual markings, or with longer spines, etc, will often cost more. Dealers' costs for shells will vary and their overheads will have been taken into consideration too. (See Bibliography p240 for a book on dealers' prices).

Many dealers subscribe to a standard shell-grading system, which will make your choice from their lists easier. These consist of the following:

Gem
A virtually flawless specimen without any breaks or flaws. The spire and any spines should be perfect, the lip unchipped and not filed. It should well cleaned without excessive oiling, and of good adult size.

Fine
An adult shell with only minor natural flaws and no more than one natural growth scar. The outer edge or lip could have one small chip or crack, and the original colour and gloss (if any) should be evident. In, for example, Murex or Thorny Oysters, very minor spine damage could be acceptable. There should be no human 'repairs', and the specimen must be well cleaned.

Fair or good
A reasonable shell, reflected in the price, which could have several flaws, be somewhat faded, bear growth scars or breaks, have broken spines or a worn lip or spire. It may also be immature, but should in general display all the characteristics of that species.

Poor
A commercial graded shell, with numerous obvious flaws, breaks, etc. Collectors will often accept this if a better specimen is not available.

Many factors will influence the status of 'common' or 'rare' and this has changed widely over the last two or three centuries. Some deep-water species, or those from a single inaccessible habitat or location, once termed rare, could now be labelled uncommon due to modern fishing/collecting methods and the increase and popularity of worldwide travel. However, many shells are indeed still rare, or very rare, and will command high prices. Areas with severe collecting restrictions (nature reserves and conservation areas) render collecting difficult, if not impossible. Shells from the Galalagos Islands are very hard to come by for this reason, and many species are endemic to those islands.

Famous, much sought-after species, like the Golden Cowrie and Glory of the Seas Cone, although one-time rarities, can still be expensive if demand exceeds supply, especially for large, perfect shells.

Shells generally should never be collected as a financial investment. Prices fluctuate, condition can deteriorate and older collections, although perhaps containing a rarity or two, will never recoup the cost originally paid out for them. Buy according to your budget and circumstances. If you like a specimen and can afford it that is good enough reason to buy!

classification and naming of seashells

Because the Phylum Mollusca is a vast and complex group of living things, it has had to be arranged in a scientific system that can be understood by everyone. Furthermore each species, like every other in the animal kingdom, bears a unique two-part Latin name.

We usually refer to natural living things by their common or colloquial name, and understandably, this can vary from country to country. We refer to 'Whelks' or 'Cockles' and elsewhere to 'Conch' and 'Clams', but this can be misleading and therefore each shell bears its own Latin name, which has been adopted worldwide and alleviates confusion. However this has not always been the case.

During times of exploration in the 16th and 17th centuries when ships returned laden from long voyages, a chaotic situation existed whereby shell names, along with most other natural things, were called one of possibly several names which led, naturally, to much confusion. It was only a matter of time before shell classification and naming was standardized and workable.

Carl Linnaeus, a Swedish naturalist, took up the challenge of sorting classification, and published, after many years' work, his momentous title, Systema Naturae in 1758. He described and listed every animal, plant and seashell known to him at that time, giving each species two Latin names, and placing species within like groups and so on. Latin was chosen because it was a dead language, and politically neutral. Hence, for the first time in history, a concise and standard system of classification had been completed. It was known as the binominal system.

This system was not, however, universally accepted until the late 18th and early 19th centuries. Common names were slow to disappear from scientific publications and it is interesting to note that shell collectors and dealers were most reluctant to adopt the new system as it was considered too 'unnecessary' and 'revolutionary'. The first of the two Latin name refers to the genus (plural genera) – a group of closely related species that starts with a capital letter. The second name, not capitalized, is the specific or species name. The generic name cannot be used for more than one group of animals, and the specific name can only be used for one species within that genus. It should therefore be obvious that there can only ever be one species called Cypraea tigris (Tiger Cowrie).

For every named shell, there is an authority, known as the author, the name of whom immediately follows the specific name in correct nomenclature. This is the scientist, biologist or layman who actually named and published a valid scientific description of the shell in question. The publication date often follows the author's name in many shell books. Therefore, it is Cypraea tigris Linne 1758. In this case the species was actually described by Linnaeus (usually shortened to Linne) and was described in 1758. His name is also the only one often abbreviated to L. 1758.

Some families are large and varied and have related genera, others only have one genus. Related families are similarly placed within superfamilies, then comes the order, occasionally the subclass, and finally the largest category, the class.

Where three Latin names occur, the final name is the sub-species – a variation close to the specific form. This third name is sometimes prefixed by an 'f. ' (form) or 'var.' (variety). It is not capitalized and the author of the sub-specific name replaces the author of the species

On close examination of dealers' lists and shell books, it will be evident that there has been much splitting of families into sub-families, genera into sub-genera, species into sub-species and variations and so on, and this can lead to more confusion. There is, however, a general trend to further simplify matters in molluscan nomenclature wherever possible, but regrettably there is always the scientist or biologist who knows better and one has to live with that!

Cypraea tigris is scientifically classified as follows:

Phylum Mollusca

Class Gastropoda

Subclass Prosobranchia

Order Mesogastropoda

Superfamily Cypraeoidea

Family Cypraeidae

Genus Cypraea

Species tigris

WORLDWIDE DISTRIBUTION OF MOLLUSCS

Many and various factors determine the distribution of seashells throughout the world's seas – water currents and depths, climatic conditions, food supply and the lifestyle of the mollusc itself. Many species occur in one specific region, while others are confined to a general area. Some species occur widespread in several oceans. The larval, veliger stage of the species Ranella olearium L. (Wandering Triton) has been carried far and wide on ocean currents, and can occur in the Mediterranean Sea, Australia, New Zealand, South and West Africa!

In the mid 19th century, Samuel Pickworth Woodward showed that the oceans could be divided up into zoogeographical provinces reflecting molluscan distribution, established on the basis that at least 50 percent of all marine shell species in each, do not occur in any other area. His 16 provinces are still generally accepted and provide a reasonable basis on which to work. The areas in parenthesis also fall into these provinces and occur in the text elsewhere as an aid to more precise location.

Aleutian North Pacific from Siberia and Southern Alaska to the Bering Sea and south to British Columbia.

Arctic North polar seas, Northern Alaska and Canada, Greenland and Northern Siberia.

Australian Western, Southern and Eastern Australia, New Zealand.

Boreal Eastern Canada, Northern and Northeastern Atlantic, North Sea.

Californian Western USA, California to Baja California.

Caribbean Gulf of Mexico, Florida, West Indies, Caribbean Sea, Venezuela, Northeastern Brazil.

Indo Pacific East Africa, Mauritius, Madagascar, Red Sea, Gulf of Oman and Arabian Gulf, Indian Ocean, India and Sri Lanka, Thailand, China Sea, Taiwan, Malaysia, Indonesia, Philippines, Papua New Guinea, Vanuatu, New Caledonia, Northern Australia, Western and South-west Pacific, Tahiti, Easter Islands, Marquesas Islands, Andaman Sea, Hawaiian Islands, Sulu Sea and Bay of Bengal.

Japonic Japan, Okinawa and Korea.

Magellanic Southern Chile and Southern Argentina.

Mediterranean Mediterranean Sea, Northwest Africa and Canary Islands

Panamic Gulf of California, West Mexico, Western Central America and Panama.

Patagonian Eastern South America, Brazil and Argentina.

Peruvian Western South America, Peru and Northern Chile.

South African South and Southeast Africa.

Transatlantic Eastern and Southeastern USA.

West African Western Africa, Senegal, Angola and Cape Verde Islands.

MAJOR GROUPS OF MARINE SNAILS

A great diversity in both shape and sculpture is evident from the families listed on pp 44–5. They range from the primitive Slit Shells along with their Limpet allies to the highly evolved Cones, Augers and Bubble Shells. Of the hundred or more families (and sub-families) that exist, 81 are listed. They include the great majority of better-known molluscs often found in amateur collections.

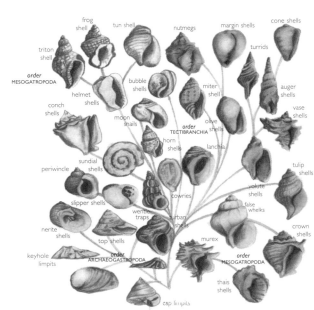

Marine Snails

Marine Bivalves

Class Gastropoda

Order Archaegastropoda
Family Slit Shells (Pleurotomariidae)
Abalones (Haliotidae)
Keyhole Limpets (Fissurellidae)
True Limpets (Acmaeidae, Patellidae)
Top Shells (Trochidae)
Turban Shells (Turbinidae)
Star Shells (Turbinidae)
Pheasant Shells (Phasianellidae)
Nerite Shells (Neritidae)

Order Mesogastropoda
Family Periwinkles (Littorinidae)
Ceriths (Cerithiidae)
Bell Clappers (Campanilidae)
Horn Shells/Mud Creepers (Potamididae)
Screw Shells (Turitellidae)
Worm Shells (Siliquariidae)
Pelican's Foot Shells (Aporrhaidae)
Spider Shells (Strombidae)
True Conch (Strombidae)
Slipper Shells (Crepidulidae)
Cap Shells (Capulidae)
Carrier Shells (Xenophoridae)
Cowries (Cypraeidae)
alse Cowries (Ovulidae & Triviidae)
Moonsnails (Naticidae)
Tun Shells (Tonnidae)
Fig Shells (Ficidae)

Helmet Shells (Cassidae)
Triton Shells (Ranellidae)
Frog Shells (Bursidae)
Wentletraps (Epitoniidae)
Purple Sea Snails (Janthinidae)

Order Neogastropoda
Family Murex Shells (Muricidae)
Rock Shells (Thaidinae)
Coral Snails (Coralliophilidae)
Whelks (Buccinidae)
Dove Shells (Columbellidae)
Nassa Mud Snails (Nassariidae)
Swamp & Melon Conch (Melongenidae)
Tulip Shells (Fasciolariidae)
Volutes (Volutidae)
Harp Shells (Harpidae)
Vase Shells (Vasidae)
Olive Shells (Olividae)
Margin Shells (Marginellidae)
Mitre Shells (Mitridae)
Nutmegs (Cancellariidae)
Cone Shells (Conidae)
Turrid Shells (Turridae)
Auger Shells (Terebridae)
Sundials (Architectonicidae)

Order Cephalaspida
Family Bubble Shells (Acteonidae, Hydatinidae, Hamineidae & Bullidae)

Class Bivalvia

Order Arcoida
Family   Ark Shells (Arcidae)
        Bittersweet Clams (Glycimerididae)

Order Mytiloida
Family   Mussels (Mytilidae)

Order Pteroida
Family   Wing Oysters (Pteriidae & Malleidae)
        Pen Shells (Pinnidae)

Order Limoida
Family   File Clams (Limidae)

Order Ostreoida
Family   Oysters (Ostreidae)
        Scallops (Pectinidae)
        Thorny Oysters (Spondylidae)
        Jingle Shells & Windowpane Oysters
        (Anomiidae & Placunidae)

Order Trigonoida
Family   Brooch Clams (Trigoniidae)

Order Veneroida
Family   Lucines & Basket Lucines (Lucinidae &
        Fimbriidae)
        Cardita Clams (Carditidae)
        Jewel Boxes (Chamidae)
        Cockles (Cardiidae)
        Giant Clams (Tridacnidae)
        Razor Shells (Solenidae & Cultellidae)
        Tellins (Tellinidae)
        Wedge Clams (Donacidae)
        Arctica Clams (Arcticidae)
        Heart Clams (Glossidae)
        Venus Clams (Veneridae)

Order Myoida
Family   Rock Borers (Pholadidae)
        Watering Pots (Clavagellidae)
        Verticord Clams (Verticordiidae)

Class Polyplacophora

Order Neoloricata
Family   Coat of Mail Shells (Ischnochitonidae)

Class Cephalopoda

Order Nautiloida
Family   Nautilus Shells (Nautilidae)

Order Sepiida
Family   Spirulas (Spirulidae)

Order Octopoda
Family   Paper Nautilus (Argonautidae)

Class Scaphopoda

Order Dentaliida
Family   Tusk Shells (Dentaliidae)

slit shells

The Pleurotomariidae, or Slit Shells (so-called because of their anal slit through which waste escapes), are an ancient group with ancestors dating back to early Cambrian times. The shells are all vegetarian, living mostly in deep waters – some to 600 metres (1,968 feet). There are about sixteen named species and many are seldom seen in amateur collections; most command high prices when available.

West Australian Slit Shell
Perotrochus westralis. Whitehead. 13cm/5in.
Fished in depths to 450m/1,500ft.
Off N.W. Australia.
Uncommon.

Emperor Slit Shell
Perotrochus hirasei Pilsbry.
10cm/4in. Taiwan & Japan.
Uncommon.

Victor Dan's Slit Shell
Perotrochus vicdani Kosuge.
5cm/2in. Philippines. Rare.

Salmiana Slit Shell
Perotrochus salmiana Rolle.
10cm/4in. Western Pacific.
Rare.

Atlantic Slit Shell
Perotrochus atlantica Rios &
Matthews. 7.5cm/3in. Brazil.
Rare.

abalones

The Haliotidae – Abalones, Ormers or Sea Ears – number in excess of 100 species. Most are edible rock-dwelling shells found in both shallow and deeper water. Many larger species are farmed commercially for seafood and the mother-of-pearl industry. Some are shown here.

Green Abalone
Haliotis fulgens Philippi.
20cm/8in. Southern
California to Mexico.
Common.

Midas Ear Abalone
Haliotis midae Linne.
15cm/6in. South Africa.
Common.

Paua Shell
Haliotis iris Martyn.
15cm/6in. New Zealand.
Popular material for shell
jewellery, inlay work etc.
Common.

Corrugated Abalone
Haliotis corrugata. Wood. 15cm/6in.
California. Common.

Giant Abalone
Haliotis gigantea Gmelin.
20cm/8in. Japan. Popular seafood
species. Common.

Donkey's Ear
Haliotis asinina Linne.
10cm/4in. Abundant Indo
Pacific species.

Staircase Abalone
Haliotis scalaris Leach.
10cm/4in. Southern & Western
Australia. Finely sculptured
interior and dorsum. Uncommon.

**European Edible
Abalone**
Haliotis tuberculata Linne.
9cm/3.5in. Sometimes known
as 'Sea Ear'. Mediterranean and
N.E. Atlantic.
Abundant.

Ribbed Abalone
Haliotis coccinea Reeve.
5cm/2in. Canary Islands.
Uncommon.

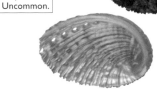

**Blood-spotted
Abalone**
Haliotis spadicea Donovan.
5cm/2in. South Africa.
Common.

Semiplicate Abalone
Haliotis semiplicata Menke.
4cm/1.5in. Uncommon. Australia
and Western Pacific.
Uncommon.

keyhole limpets

Fissurellidae are known as Keyhole Limpets because of their characteristic dorsal hole or slot, which is used for excretion. They are a large family of primitive shells enjoying worldwide distribution. They are egg-laying vegetarians.

Great Keyhole Limpet
Megathura crenulata Sowerby.
12cm/4.75in. One of the largest Keyhole Limpets. California to Mexico. Common.

Thick Keyhole Limpet
Fissurella crassa Lamarck.
8cm/3.25in. Western Central to South America. Common.

Giant Keyhole Limpet
Fissurella maxima Sowerby.
12cm/4.75in. Rocky reef dweller. Western South America. Common.

Juke's Keyhole Limpet
Diodora jukesi Reeve.
4cm/1.5in. Southern Australia. Common.

Double-edged Keyhole Limpet
Fissurella aperta Sowerby.
3cm/1.25in. Variable dorsal patterns. South Africa. Common.

Italian Keyhole Limpet
Diodora italica DeFrance.
2.5cm/1in. Northern Mediterranean Sea. Common.

Mouse Keyhole Limpet.
Diodora mus Reeve.
2cm/0.75in. China Sea, Japan. Common.

true limpets

A large family (Patellidae) all of which are vegetarian and live generally sedentary lives firmly attached to rocks in shallow water. Not particularly popular with collectors, although many species have highly coloured and patterned interiors.

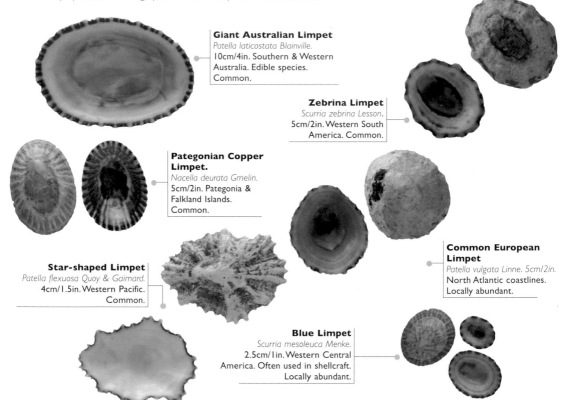

Giant Australian Limpet
Patella laticostata Blainville.
10cm/4in. Southern & Western
Australia. Edible species.
Common.

Zebrina Limpet
Scurria zebrina Lesson.
5cm/2in. Western South
America. Common.

Pategonian Copper Limpet.
Nacella deurata Gmelin.
5cm/2in. Pategonia &
Falkland Islands.
Common.

Common European Limpet
Patella vulgata Linne. 5cm/2in.
North Atlantic coastlines.
Locally abundant.

Star-shaped Limpet
Patella flexuosa Quoy & Gaimard.
4cm/1.5in. Western Pacific.
Common.

Blue Limpet
Scurria mesoleuca Menke.
2.5cm/1in. Western Central
America. Often used in shellcraft.
Locally abundant.

SOUTH AFRICAN LIMPETS

The South African coastline offers an ideal habitat for limpets, and all of the species shown here are endemic.

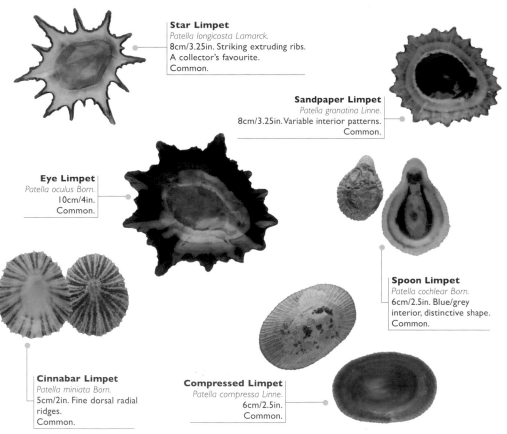

Star Limpet
Patella longicosta Lamarck.
8cm/3.25in. Striking extruding ribs.
A collector's favourite.
Common.

Sandpaper Limpet
Patella granatina Linne.
8cm/3.25in. Variable interior patterns.
Common.

Eye Limpet
Patella oculus Born.
10cm/4in.
Common.

Spoon Limpet
Patella cochlear Born.
6cm/2.5in. Blue/grey
interior, distinctive shape.
Common.

Cinnabar Limpet
Patella miniata Born.
5cm/2in. Fine dorsal radial
ridges.
Common.

Compressed Limpet
Patella compressa Linne.
6cm/2.5in.
Common.

top shells

A large family – some hundreds of mostly small species – the Trochidae, have a worldwide distribution. Most are herbivores and some feed on sponges. All are conical or top-shaped and possess horny operculae. All are nacreous inside, and the larger species are used in the mother-of-pearl trade.

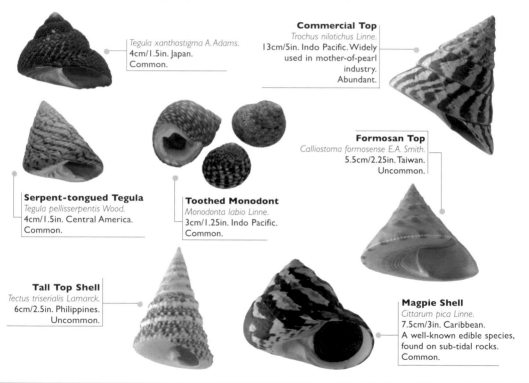

Tegula xanthostigma A. Adams.
4cm/1.5in. Japan.
Common.

Commercial Top
Trochus nilotichus Linne.
13cm/5in. Indo Pacific. Widely
used in mother-of-pearl
industry.
Abundant.

Formosan Top
Calliostoma formosense E.A. Smith.
5.5cm/2.25in. Taiwan.
Uncommon.

Serpent-tongued Tegula
Tegula pellisserpentis Wood.
4cm/1.5in. Central America.
Common.

Toothed Monodont
Monodonta labio Linne.
3cm/1.25in. Indo Pacific.
Common.

Tall Top Shell
Tectus triserialis Lamarck.
6cm/2.5in. Philippines.
Uncommon.

Magpie Shell
Cittarum pica Linne.
7.5cm/3in. Caribbean.
A well-known edible species,
found on sub-tidal rocks.
Common.

NEW ZEALAND TOPS

New Zealand boasts numerous Top Shells, most endemic to the islands and popular collector's items.

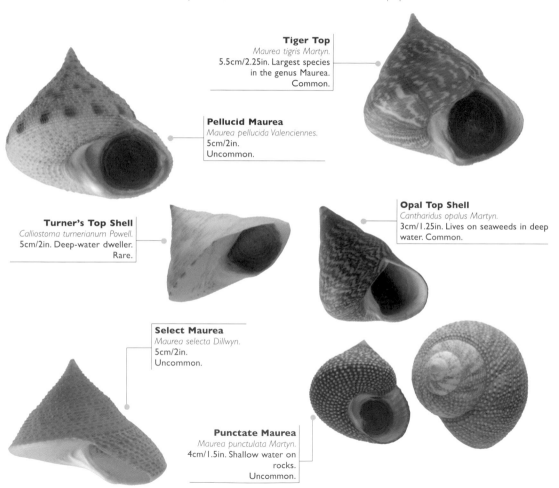

Tiger Top
Maurea tigris Martyn.
5.5cm/2.25in. Largest species
in the genus Maurea.
Common.

Pellucid Maurea
Maurea pellucida Valenciennes.
5cm/2in.
Uncommon.

Opal Top Shell
Cantharidus opalus Martyn.
3cm/1.25in. Lives on seaweeds in deep
water. Common.

Turner's Top Shell
Calliostoma turnerianum Powell.
5cm/2in. Deep-water dweller.
Rare.

Select Maurea
Maurea selecta Dillwyn.
5cm/2in.
Uncommon.

Punctate Maurea
Maurea punctulata Martyn.
4cm/1.5in. Shallow water on
rocks.
Uncommon.

SOUTH AFRICAN TOPS

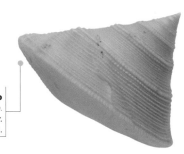

Scott's Top
Calliostoma scotti Kilburn.
4cm/1.5in. Deep-water dweller.
Uncommon.

Rose-based Top
Oxystele sinensis Gmelin.
4cm/1.5in. Inter-tidal rock pools.
Common.

Tiger Top
Oxystele tigerina Anton.
3cm/1.25in.
Common.

South African Top
Calliostoma africanum Bartsch.
2cm/0.75in. Deep-water dweller.
Uncommon.

Ornate Top
Calliostoma ornatum Lamarck.
2.5cm/1in.
Uncommon.

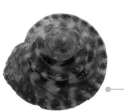

Keeled Top
Clanculus miniatus Anton.
1.5cm/0.5in.
Uncommon.

UNCOMMON AND RARE TOP SHELLS

These mostly deep-water species are prized by Top Shell collectors.

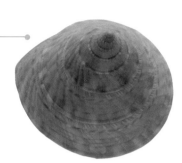

Keeled Australian Top
Calliostoma ciliaris Menke.
4cm/1.5in. Western Australia.
Uncommon.

Superb Gaza
Gaza superba Dall.
4cm/1.5in. Gulf of Mexico/West
Indies. A sought-after collector's
item and deep-water
rarity.

Bularra Top
Astele bularra Garrard.
2.5cm/1in. Southern and Eastern
Australia. Deep water,
uncommon.

Springer's Top
Calliostoma springeri Clench & Turner.
3cm/1.25in. Northern Gulf of Mexico.
A deep-water
rarity.

Monile Top
Calliostoma monile Reeve.
2cm/0.75in. Western Australia.
A shallow-water sponge-dweller.
Uncommon.

Ringed Top
Calliostoma annulatum Lightfoot.
2.5cm/1in. California.
Uncommon.

pheasant shells

The Phasianellidae and Tricoliidae families contain relatively few species. They are vegetarian, smooth and often highly patterned and colourful. They live in warm, shallow seas. The operculae are all usually chalky white. The Red Pheasant is used in shellcraft.

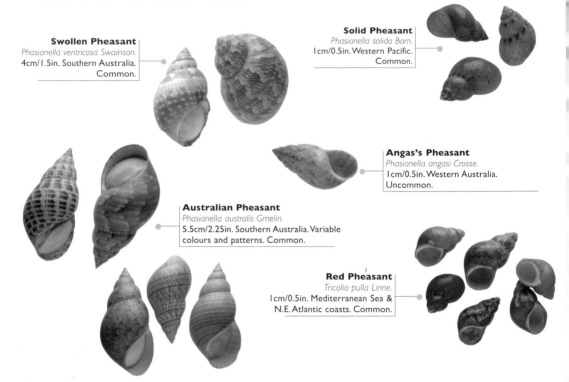

Swollen Pheasant
Phasianella ventricosa Swainson.
4cm/1.5in. Southern Australia. Common.

Solid Pheasant
Phasianella solida Born.
1cm/0.5in. Western Pacific. Common.

Angas's Pheasant
Phasianella angasi Crosse.
1cm/0.5in. Western Australia. Uncommon.

Australian Pheasant
Phasianella australis Gmelin.
5.5cm/2.25in. Southern Australia. Variable colours and patterns. Common.

Red Pheasant
Tricolia pulla Linne.
1cm/0.5in. Mediterranean Sea & N.E. Atlantic coasts. Common.

delphinula or dolphin shells

The large Turban Shell family is split into sub-families. The Dolphin Shells (Angariinae) are an attractive group, some of which bear long and delicate spines. All have horny operculae.

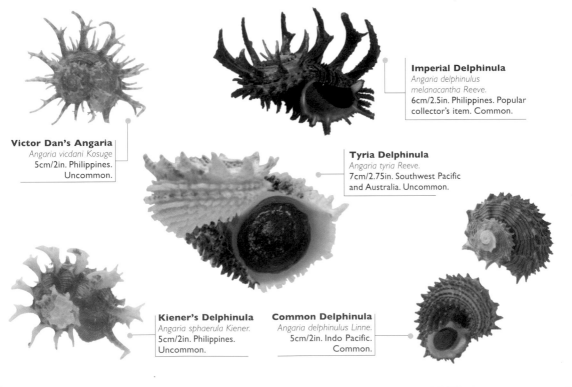

Imperial Delphinula
Angaria delphinulus melanacantha Reeve.
6cm/2.5in. Philippines. Popular collector's item. Common.

Victor Dan's Angaria
Angaria vicdani Kosuge
5cm/2in. Philippines. Uncommon.

Tyria Delphinula
Angaria tyria Reeve.
7cm/2.75in. Southwest Pacific and Australia. Uncommon.

Kiener's Delphinula
Angaria sphaerula Kiener.
5cm/2in. Philippines. Uncommon.

Common Delphinula
Angaria delphinulus Linne.
5cm/2in. Indo Pacific. Common.

true turban shells

The true Turbans (Turbininae) are a large sub-family of several hundred species. All have thick, shelly operculae and are vegetarian. Most dwell in the shallow waters of warm tropical seas. The Green Turban is the largest species and many are shipped from East Africa to the Far East for use in the mother-of-pearl industry.

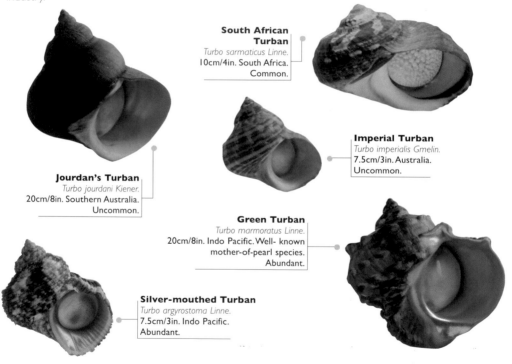

South African Turban
Turbo sarmaticus Linne.
10cm/4in. South Africa.
Common.

Imperial Turban
Turbo imperialis Gmelin.
7.5cm/3in. Australia.
Uncommon.

Jourdan's Turban
Turbo jourdani Kiener.
20cm/8in. Southern Australia.
Uncommon.

Green Turban
Turbo marmoratus Linne.
20cm/8in. Indo Pacific. Well- known
mother-of-pearl species.
Abundant.

Silver-mouthed Turban
Turbo argyrostoma Linne.
7.5cm/3in. Indo Pacific.
Abundant.

TURBAN SHELLS

Reeve's Turban
Turbo reevei Philippi.
4cm/1.5in. Philippines. Variable colours and patterns.
Common.

Whitley's Turban
Ninella whitleyi Iredale.
5.5cm/2.25in. Australia.
Distinctive operculum.
Uncommon.

Green-ridged Turban
Turbo speciosus Reeve.
5cm/2in. Southeastern Australia.
Common.

Smooth Moon Turban
Lunella cinerea Born.
3cm/1.25in. Indo Pacific.
Common.

Crinkly Turban
Turbo laminiferous Reeve.
3cm/1.25in. Northern Australia to Papua New Guinea.
Common.

Gruner's Turban
Turbo gruneri Philippi.
4cm/1.5in. Southern & Western Australia.
Uncommon.

STAR SHELLS

A sub-family of the Turbans (Astraeinae) and popular with collectors.

Anderson's Star Shell
Bolma andersoni E.A. Smith.
7.5cm/3in. South Africa.
A rare deep-water species.

Modest Bolma
Bolma modesta Reeve.
5cm/2in. Taiwan to Japan.
Uncommon.

Taylor's Star Shell
Bolma tayloriana E.A. Smith.
7.5cm/3in. South Africa.
Uncommon deep-water species.

Blue-mouthed Star Shell
Astraea stellare Gmelin.
4cm/1.5in. Western Australia.
Unique turquoise-blue operculum.
Common.

Olfer's Star
Astraea olfersii Philippi.
4cm/1.5in. Brazil.
Uncommon.

Bridled Bolma
Bolma aureola Hedley.
7.5cm/3in. Eastern Australia.
Uncommon.

Busch's Star Shell
Astraea buschi Philippi.
6cm/2.5in.
Tropical West America.
Uncommon.

Carved Star Shell
Astraea caelata Gmelin.
5cm/2in. Caribbean.
Common.

STAR SHELLS

Flawless specimens of these shells are difficult to obtain; the Girgyllus Star has particularly fragile spines.

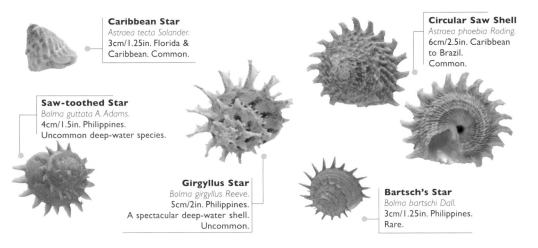

Caribbean Star
Astraea tecta Solander.
3cm/1.25in. Florida &
Caribbean. Common.

Circular Saw Shell
Astraea phoebia Roding.
6cm/2.5in. Caribbean
to Brazil.
Common.

Saw-toothed Star
Bolma guttata A. Adams.
4cm/1.5in. Philippines.
Uncommon deep-water species.

Girgyllus Star
Bolma girgyllus Reeve.
5cm/2in. Philippines.
A spectacular deep-water shell.
Uncommon.

Bartsch's Star
Bolma bartschi Dall.
3cm/1.25in. Philippines.
Rare.

LONG-SPINE STAR SHELLS

Unique shells with fantastic elongated spines; these shells inhabit very deep water to about 500 metres (1,640 feet).

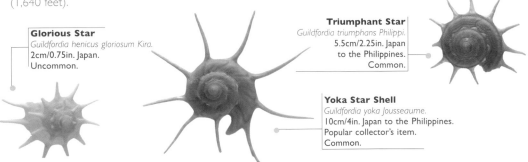

Glorious Star
Guildfordia henicus gloriosum Kira.
2cm/0.75in. Japan.
Uncommon.

Triumphant Star
Guildfordia triumphans Philippi.
5.5cm/2.25in. Japan
to the Philippines.
Common.

Yoka Star Shell
Guildfordia yoka Jousseaume.
10cm/4in. Japan to the Philippines.
Popular collector's item.
Common.

nerite snails

The Neritidae are a small family of about 50 species and are not particularly popular with collectors, although the Bleeding-tooth and the Candy Nerite are well known. With close-fitting operculae, the shells can store water within the shell and can often survive for extended periods without moisture.

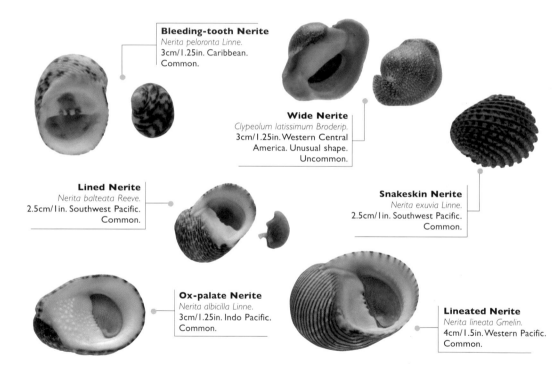

Bleeding-tooth Nerite
Nerita peloronta Linne.
3cm/1.25in. Caribbean.
Common.

Wide Nerite
Clypeolum latissimum Broderip.
3cm/1.25in. Western Central
America. Unusual shape.
Uncommon.

Lined Nerite
Nerita balteata Reeve.
2.5cm/1in. Southwest Pacific.
Common.

Snakeskin Nerite
Nerita exuvia Linne.
2.5cm/1in. Southwest Pacific.
Common.

Ox-palate Nerite
Nerita albicilla Linne.
3cm/1.25in. Indo Pacific.
Common.

Lineated Nerite
Nerita lineata Gmelin.
4cm/1.5in. Western Pacific.
Common.

COLOURFUL NERITES

The Emerald Nerite has been used extensively in shellcraft, although nowadays it is difficult to obtain in quantity.

Emerald Nerite
Smaragdia viridis Linne.
6mm/0.25in. Philippines & Western Pacific.
Common.

Candy Nerite
Neritina communis Quoy & Gaimard.
1cm/0.5in. Philippines. Extremely variable.
Abundant.

Polished Nerite
Nerita polita Linne.
2.5cm/1in. Indo Pacific. Variable patterns
and colours.
Common.

PERIWINKLES

This is a group of about 100 species, called Littorinidae. They are vegetarian and inhabit rocky shores; some species occur in mangrove swamps.

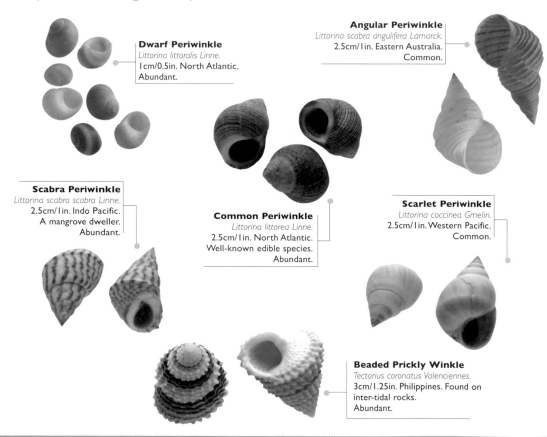

Dwarf Periwinkle
Littorina littoralis Linne.
1cm/0.5in. North Atlantic.
Abundant.

Angular Periwinkle
Littorina scabra angulifera Lamarck.
2.5cm/1in. Eastern Australia.
Common.

Scabra Periwinkle
Littorina scabra scabra Linne.
2.5cm/1in. Indo Pacific.
A mangrove dweller.
Abundant.

Common Periwinkle
Littorina littorea Linne.
2.5cm/1in. North Atlantic.
Well-known edible species.
Abundant.

Scarlet Periwinkle
Littorina coccinea Gmelin.
2.5cm/1in. Western Pacific.
Common.

Beaded Prickly Winkle
Tectarius coronatus Valenciennes.
3cm/1.25in. Philippines. Found on
inter-tidal rocks.
Abundant.

BELL CLAPPERS

This is the only surviving species of a once very large family of at least 700, dating back to early fossil times. Many fossil species have been found in the Paris Basin – one species growing to 50cm/20in

The Bell Clapper in the family Campanilidae is the only surviving species. It resembles a fossil, being chalky-white in appearance. It is only found in Australia.

Australian Bell Clapper
Campanile symbolicum Iredale.
15cm/6in. Southwestern
Australia. Uncommon.

Giant Worm Shell
Siliquaria ponderosa Morch.
25cm/10in. Taiwan, Indo
Pacific. Uncommon.

Scaled Worm Shell
Siliquaria cumingi Morch.
20cm/8in. Taiwan to the
Philippines. Uncommon

WORM SHELLS

These bizarre shells, in the family Siliquariidae, are a small group that resemble worm tubes. They live mostly in warm tropical waters in colonies and clumps, or are attached singly to rocks and shells.

CERITH SHELLS

The Cerithiidae are mostly small shells, living generally in warm, shallow tropical waters in sandy substrates. Not a popular collector's family.

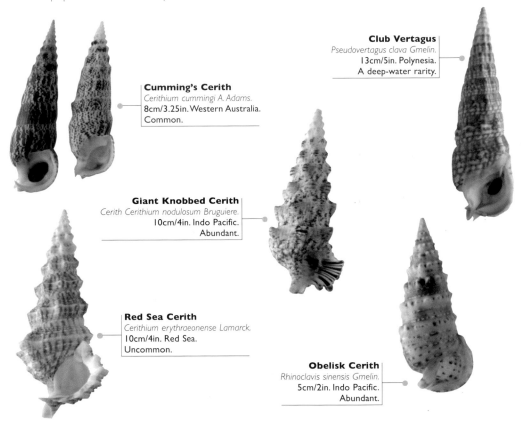

Club Vertagus
Pseudovertagus clava Gmelin.
13cm/5in. Polynesia.
A deep-water rarity.

Cumming's Cerith
Cerithium cummingi A. Adams.
8cm/3.25in. Western Australia.
Common.

Giant Knobbed Cerith
Cerith Cerithium nodulosum Bruguiere.
10cm/4in. Indo Pacific.
Abundant.

Red Sea Cerith
Cerithium erythraeonense Lamarck.
10cm/4in. Red Sea.
Uncommon.

Obelisk Cerith
Rhinoclavis sinensis Gmelin.
5cm/2in. Indo Pacific.
Abundant.

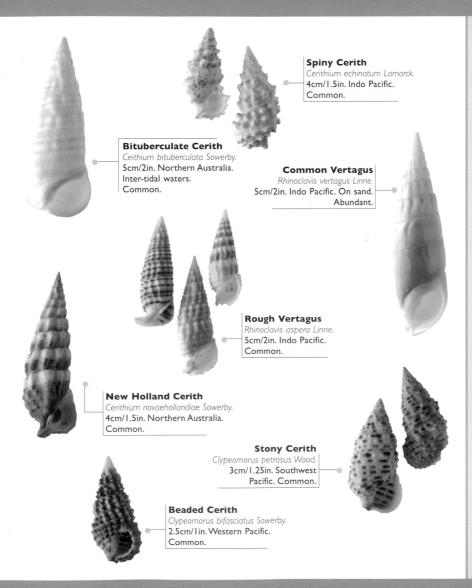

Spiny Cerith
Cerithium echinatum Lamarck.
4cm/1.5in. Indo Pacific.
Common.

Bituberculate Cerith
Ceithium bituberculata Sowerby.
5cm/2in. Northern Australia.
Inter-tidal waters.
Common.

Common Vertagus
Rhinoclavis vertagus Linne.
5cm/2in. Indo Pacific. On sand.
Abundant.

Rough Vertagus
Rhinoclavis aspera Linne.
5cm/2in. Indo Pacific.
Common.

New Holland Cerith
Cerithium novaehollandiae Sowerby.
4cm/1.5in. Northern Australia.
Common.

Stony Cerith
Clypeomorus petrosus Wood.
3cm/1.25in. Southwest
Pacific. Common.

Beaded Cerith
Clypeomorus bifasciatus Sowerby.
2.5cm/1in. Western Pacific.
Common.

HORN SHELLS

The Potamididae family, also known as Mud Creepers, due to their general habitat of warm, muddy brackish waters, is a group of mostly brown, pointed and conical shells. Of limited interest to collectors.

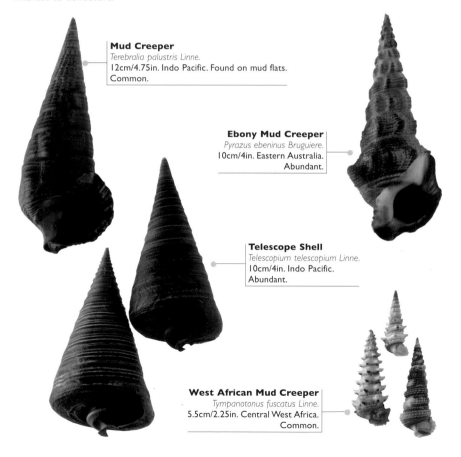

Mud Creeper
Terebralia palustris Linne.
12cm/4.75in. Indo Pacific. Found on mud flats.
Common.

Ebony Mud Creeper
Pyrazus ebeninus Bruguiere.
10cm/4in. Eastern Australia.
Abundant.

Telescope Shell
Telescopium telescopium Linne.
10cm/4in. Indo Pacific.
Abundant.

West African Mud Creeper
Tympanotonus fuscatus Linne.
5.5cm/2.25in. Central West Africa.
Common.

SCREW SHELLS

Mostly tall, tightly coiled shells. Many species occur in Western America and West Africa. A family of about 100, the Turritellidae are vegetarian and live in offshore waters in coarse sand or mud.

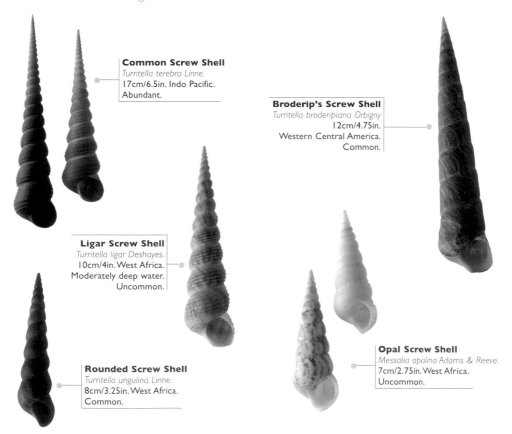

Common Screw Shell
Turritella terebra Linne.
17cm/6.5in. Indo Pacific.
Abundant.

Broderip's Screw Shell
Turritella broderipiana Orbigny
12cm/4.75in.
Western Central America.
Common.

Ligar Screw Shell
Turritella ligar Deshayes.
10cm/4in. West Africa.
Moderately deep water.
Uncommon.

Rounded Screw Shell
Turritella ungulina Linne.
8cm/3.25in. West Africa.
Common.

Opal Screw Shell
Messalia opalina Adams & Reeve.
7cm/2.75in. West Africa.
Uncommon.

SCREW SHELLS

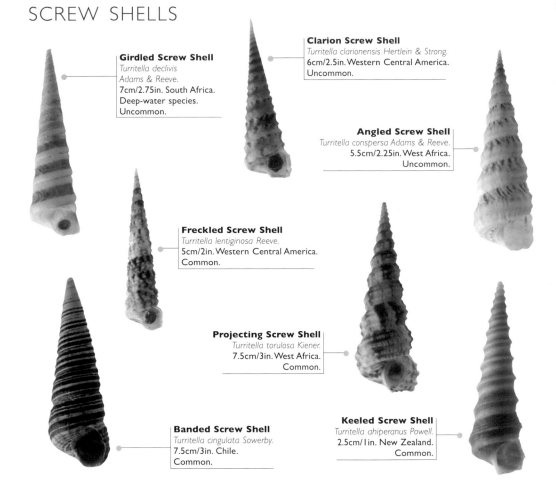

Girdled Screw Shell
*Turritella declivis
Adams & Reeve.*
7cm/2.75in. South Africa.
Deep-water species.
Uncommon.

Clarion Screw Shell
Turritella clarionensis Hertlein & Strong.
6cm/2.5in. Western Central America.
Uncommon.

Angled Screw Shell
Turritella conspersa Adams & Reeve.
5.5cm/2.25in. West Africa.
Uncommon.

Freckled Screw Shell
Turritella lentiginosa Reeve.
5cm/2in. Western Central America.
Common.

Projecting Screw Shell
Turritella torulosa Kiener.
7.5cm/3in. West Africa.
Common.

Banded Screw Shell
Turritella cingulata Sowerby.
7.5cm/3in. Chile.
Common.

Keeled Screw Shell
Turritella ahiperanus Powell.
2.5cm/1in. New Zealand.
Common.

PELICAN'S FOOT SHELLS

A family of only six species, the Aporrhaidae occur in the cooler waters of the North Atlantic and the Mediterranean. Many strangely shaped fossil species exist. The American Pelican's Foot is generally the more difficult to obtain, due to its deep-water habitat (to about 600 metres/1,968 feet). They all live in sandy substrates.

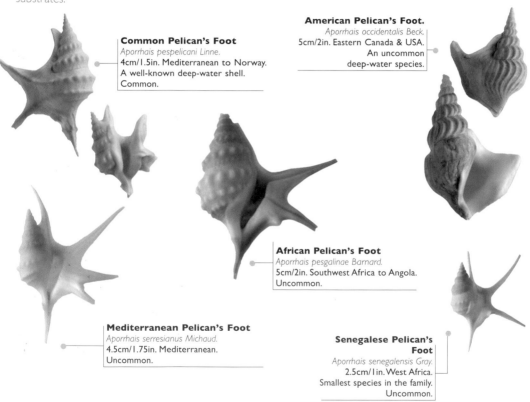

Common Pelican's Foot
Aporrhais pespelicani Linne.
4cm/1.5in. Mediterranean to Norway.
A well-known deep-water shell.
Common.

American Pelican's Foot.
Aporrhais occidentalis Beck.
5cm/2in. Eastern Canada & USA.
An uncommon
deep-water species.

African Pelican's Foot
Aporrhais pesgalinae Barnard.
5cm/2in. Southwest Africa to Angola.
Uncommon.

Mediterranean Pelican's Foot
Aporrhais serresianus Michaud.
4.5cm/1.75in. Mediterranean.
Uncommon.

**Senegalese Pelican's
Foot**
Aporrhais senegalensis Gray.
2.5cm/1in. West Africa.
Smallest species in the family.
Uncommon.

SPIDER CONCH SHELLS

These well-known shells with flaring lips and long projecting spines are a popular collector's family. They are part of the large group of Conch shells known as the Strombidae. Some of the larger species are shown here.

Giant Spider Conch
Lambis truncata Humphrey.
30cm/12in. Indo Pacific. Largest species in the genus. Common.

Chiragra Spider Conch
Lambis chiragra chiragra Linne.
20cm/8in. Indo Pacific. Common.

POPULAR SPIDER CONCH

The Orange Spider Conch has some uncommon sub-species – one, a giant form from the Central Pacific and is uncommon. The Finger Spider Conch is the rarer species here.

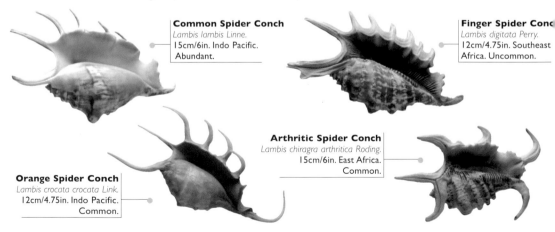

Common Spider Conch
Lambis lambis Linne.
15cm/6in. Indo Pacific. Abundant.

Finger Spider Conch
Lambis digitata Perry.
12cm/4.75in. Southeast Africa. Uncommon.

Orange Spider Conch
Lambis crocata crocata Link.
12cm/4.75in. Indo Pacific. Common.

Arthritic Spider Conch
Lambis chiragra arthritica Roding.
15cm/6in. East Africa. Common.

TRUE CONCH

A large, diverse family, the Strombidae have the characteristic Stromboid Notch – an indentation at the anterior end of the shell through which the animal protrudes its stalked eye. All the Conch described here are uncommon or rare collector's favourites.

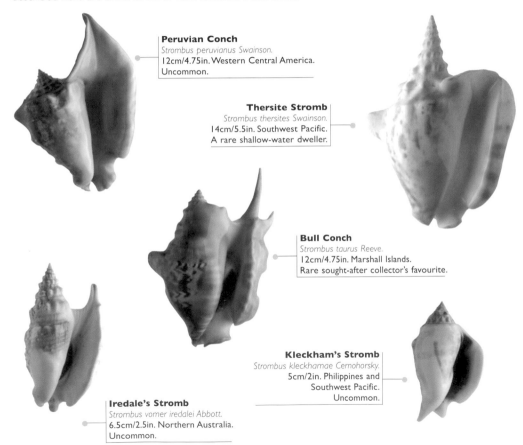

Peruvian Conch
Strombus peruvianus Swainson.
12cm/4.75in. Western Central America.
Uncommon.

Thersite Stromb
Strombus thersites Swainson.
14cm/5.5in. Southwest Pacific.
A rare shallow-water dweller.

Bull Conch
Strombus taurus Reeve.
12cm/4.75in. Marshall Islands.
Rare sought-after collector's favourite.

Kleckham's Stromb
Strombus kleckhamae Cernohorsky.
5cm/2in. Philippines and
Southwest Pacific.
Uncommon.

Iredale's Stromb
Strombus vomer iredalei Abbott.
6.5cm/2.5in. Northern Australia.
Uncommon.

WELL-KNOWN CONCH

Seen in most general collections, these species are common. The large Queen Conch is now a protected species due to many years of over-harvesting for the seafood industry and can only be obtained with special import licences. Likewise the Three-knobbed Conch inhabits protected waters and few can be readily obtained.

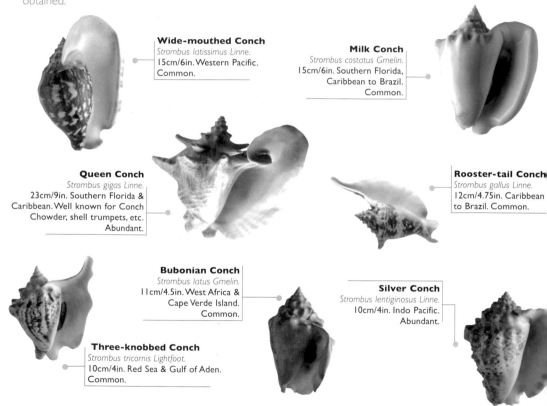

Wide-mouthed Conch
Strombus latissimus Linne.
15cm/6in. Western Pacific.
Common.

Milk Conch
Strombus costatus Gmelin.
15cm/6in. Southern Florida,
Caribbean to Brazil.
Common.

Queen Conch
Strombus gigas Linne.
23cm/9in. Southern Florida &
Caribbean. Well known for Conch
Chowder, shell trumpets, etc.
Abundant.

Rooster-tail Conch
Strombus gallus Linne.
12cm/4.75in. Caribbean
to Brazil. Common.

Bubonian Conch
Strombus latus Gmelin.
11cm/4.5in. West Africa &
Cape Verde Island.
Common.

Silver Conch
Strombus lentiginosus Linne.
10cm/4in. Indo Pacific.
Abundant.

Three-knobbed Conch
Strombus tricornis Lightfoot.
10cm/4in. Red Sea & Gulf of Aden.
Common.

WELL-KNOWN CONCH

Most of these shells are common Strombs, but the Lister's Conch was for many years a great rarity, only becoming available to collectors during the late 1970s.

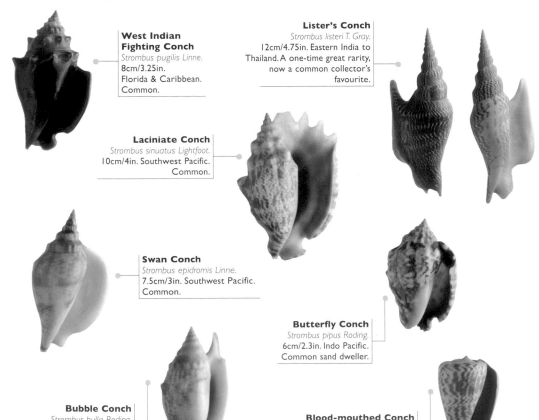

West Indian Fighting Conch
Strombus pugilis Linne.
8cm/3.25in.
Florida & Caribbean.
Common.

Lister's Conch
Strombus listeri T. Gray.
12cm/4.75in. Eastern India to Thailand. A one-time great rarity, now a common collector's favourite.

Laciniate Conch
Strombus sinuatus Lightfoot.
10cm/4in. Southwest Pacific.
Common.

Swan Conch
Strombus epidromis Linne.
7.5cm/3in. Southwest Pacific.
Common.

Butterfly Conch
Strombus pipus Roding.
6cm/2.3in. Indo Pacific.
Common sand dweller.

Bubble Conch
Strombus bulla Roding.
6cm/2.5in. Western Pacific.
Common.

Blood-mouthed Conch
Strombus luhuanus Linne.
5cm/2in. Indo Pacific.
Abundant.

TIBIA SHELLS

Although part of the Strombidae, these shells are structurally very different from the True Conch, with long siphonal canals, and generally lighter in weight. A moderately deep-water species, the Spindle Tibia is fished quite often with perfect spire and canal.

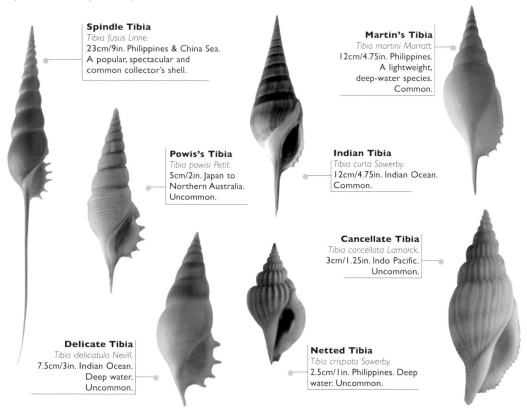

Spindle Tibia
Tibia fusus Linne.
23cm/9in. Philippines & China Sea.
A popular, spectacular and
common collector's shell.

Martin's Tibia
Tibia martini Marratt.
12cm/4.75in. Philippines.
A lightweight,
deep-water species.
Common.

Powis's Tibia
Tibia powisi Petit.
5cm/2in. Japan to
Northern Australia.
Uncommon.

Indian Tibia
Tibia curta Sowerby.
12cm/4.75in. Indian Ocean.
Common.

Cancellate Tibia
Tibia cancellata Lamarck.
3cm/1.25in. Indo Pacific.
Uncommon.

Delicate Tibia
Tibia delicatula Nevill.
7.5cm/3in. Indian Ocean.
Deep water.
Uncommon.

Netted Tibia
Tibia crispata Sowerby.
2.5cm/1in. Philippines. Deep
water. Uncommon.

CAP, SLIPPER AND CUP & SAUCER SHELLS

The Crepidulidae are a smallish group of Gastropods, which live either on rocks or on the backs of other molluscs. They all possess a peculiar plate located inside the main shell that protects the soft organs. They are distributed globally and filter-feed on vegetable matter.

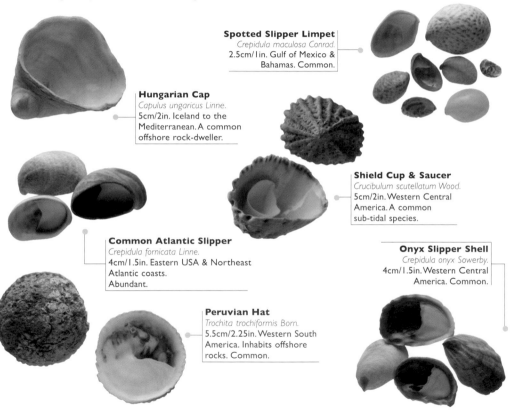

Spotted Slipper Limpet
Crepidula maculosa Conrad.
2.5cm/1in. Gulf of Mexico &
Bahamas. Common.

Hungarian Cap
Capulus ungaricus Linne.
5cm/2in. Iceland to the
Mediterranean. A common
offshore rock-dweller.

Shield Cup & Saucer
Crucibulum scutellatum Wood.
5cm/2in. Western Central
America. A common
sub-tidal species.

Common Atlantic Slipper
Crepidula fornicata Linne.
4cm/1.5in. Eastern USA & Northeast
Atlantic coasts.
Abundant.

Onyx Slipper Shell
Crepidula onyx Sowerby.
4cm/1.5in. Western Central
America. Common.

Peruvian Hat
Trochita trochiformis Born.
5.5cm/2.25in. Western South
America. Inhabits offshore
rocks. Common.

CARRIER SHELLS

The Carrier Shells, or Xenophoridae, are unique shells that use their foot to attach dead shells, shell debris and rocks, pebbles or corals to themselves. The following are some possible reasons for their behaviour: as camouflage against predators; to add rigidity and strength to a fragile shell; to stop the shell from sinking into its habitat – muddy substrates. The Sunburst Carrier is usually devoid of attachments, and perfect specimens are rarely collected. Measurements are for mature shells without attachments.

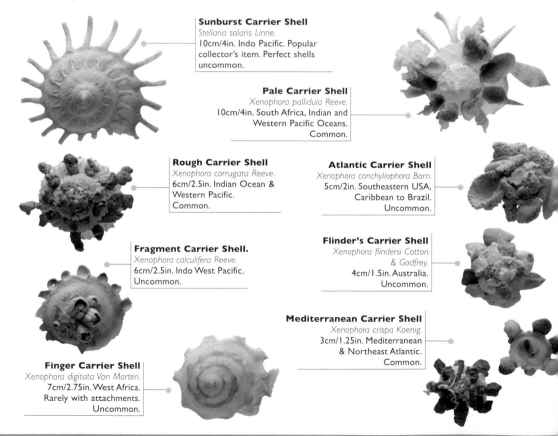

Sunburst Carrier Shell
Stellaria solaris Linne.
10cm/4in. Indo Pacific. Popular collector's item. Perfect shells uncommon.

Pale Carrier Shell
Xenophora pallidula Reeve.
10cm/4in. South Africa, Indian and Western Pacific Oceans.
Common.

Rough Carrier Shell
Xenophora corrugata Reeve.
6cm/2.5in. Indian Ocean & Western Pacific.
Common.

Atlantic Carrier Shell
Xenophora conchyliophora Born.
5cm/2in. Southeastern USA, Caribbean to Brazil.
Uncommon.

Fragment Carrier Shell.
Xenophora calculifera Reeve.
6cm/2.5in. Indo West Pacific.
Uncommon.

Flinder's Carrier Shell
Xenophora flindersi Cotton & Godfrey.
4cm/1.5in. Australia.
Uncommon.

Mediterranean Carrier Shell
Xenophora crispa Koenig.
3cm/1.25in. Mediterranean & Northeast Atlantic.
Common.

Finger Carrier Shell
Xenophora digitata Von Marten.
7cm/2.75in. West Africa.
Rarely with attachments.
Uncommon.

cowie shells

The Cowries – Cypraeidae – are probably the most well known and popular of all shells. The sheer beauty of their colour and pattern and the smoothness of their porcelain-like shells attracts an interest that is second to none amongst collectors the world over.

Most of the 200 or more species live in shallow waters of warm, tropical seas and are abundant on coral reefs, where possibly seventy percent of all Cowries live.

The female lays male-fertilized eggs and 'broods' them for up to four weeks. When hatched, there is a veliger or larval stage with most species, which transforms later into the 'bulla' stage when the developing Cowrie shell is thin and oval in shape. Gradually the shell thickens to arrive at the mature form of a hard, glossy shell. It is in the latter stages of maturity and adulthood that the last layers of pattern are laid down and it becomes recognizable as a distinct species. The mantle produces the vibrant colours and patterns and envelopes the shell, its sides meeting over the dorsum, producing a marked line or break in the pattern, known as the dorsal line.

Cowries are active at night when feeding and are both herbivore and carnivore.

Many species are abundant and live in shallow waters, but rarer shells inhabit deeper water, or, as in some instances, remote corners of the world in very restricted habitats.

Species such as the Leucodon and Broderip's Cowries have only become available to amateur collectors during the last ten to fifteen years. They are still expensive however, costing hundreds of pounds.

SMALLER INDO-PACIFIC COWIES

These shells are all coral-reef dwellers.

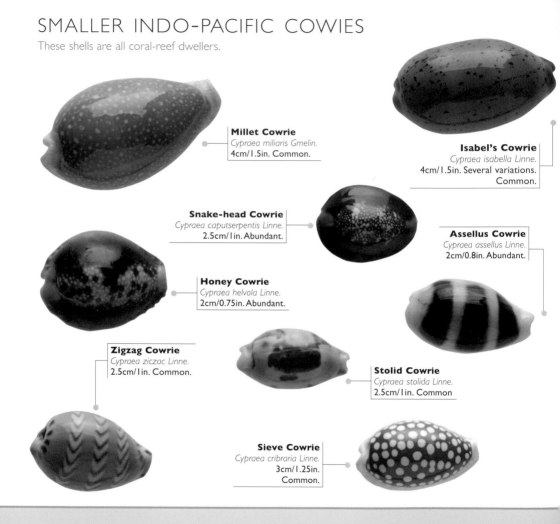

Millet Cowrie
Cypraea miliaris Gmelin.
4cm/1.5in. Common.

Isabel's Cowrie
Cypraea isabella Linne.
4cm/1.5in. Several variations.
Common.

Snake-head Cowrie
Cypraea caputserpentis Linne.
2.5cm/1in. Abundant.

Assellus Cowrie
Cypraea assellus Linne.
2cm/0.8in. Abundant.

Honey Cowrie
Cypraea helvola Linne.
2cm/0.75in. Abundant.

Zigzag Cowrie
Cypraea ziczac Linne.
2.5cm/1in. Common.

Stolid Cowrie
Cypraea stolida Linne.
2.5cm/1in. Common

Sieve Cowrie
Cypraea cribraria Linne.
3cm/1.25in.
Common.

LARGER INDO-PACIFIC COWIES

The Tiger Cowrie is well known to everyone. The Map Cowrie comes in various forms from different localities.

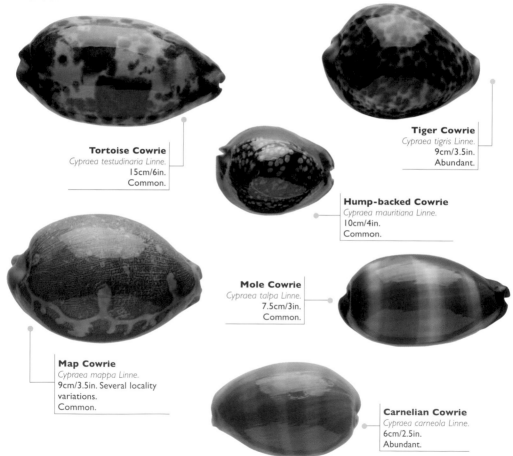

Tortoise Cowrie
Cypraea testudinaria Linne.
15cm/6in.
Common.

Tiger Cowrie
Cypraea tigris Linne.
9cm/3.5in.
Abundant.

Hump-backed Cowrie
Cypraea mauritiana Linne.
10cm/4in.
Common.

Mole Cowrie
Cypraea talpa Linne.
7.5cm/3in.
Common.

Map Cowrie
Cypraea mappa Linne.
9cm/3.5in. Several locality variations.
Common.

Carnelian Cowrie
Cypraea carneola Linne.
6cm/2.5in.
Abundant.

COWIES OF THE MEDITERRANEAN, RED SEA AND ARABIA

The Red Sea is now a conservation area, making collecting live specimens virtually impossible, although some are possibly taken under licence. Pollution in the Mediterranean Sea is taking its toll on marine life and affecting molluscan populations. Consequently, some common species are now becoming scarce.

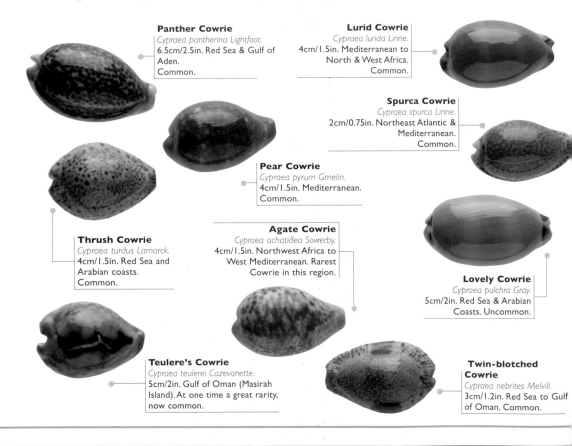

Panther Cowrie
Cypraea pantherina Lightfoot.
6.5cm/2.5in. Red Sea & Gulf of Aden.
Common.

Lurid Cowrie
Cypraea lurida Linne.
4cm/1.5in. Mediterranean to North & West Africa.
Common.

Spurca Cowrie
Cypraea spurca Linne.
2cm/0.75in. Northeast Atlantic & Mediterranean.
Common.

Pear Cowrie
Cypraea pyrum Gmelin.
4cm/1.5in. Mediterranean.
Common.

Thrush Cowrie
Cypraea turdus Lamarck.
4cm/1.5in. Red Sea and Arabian coasts.
Common.

Agate Cowrie
Cypraea achatidea Sowerby.
4cm/1.5in. Northwest Africa to West Mediterranean. Rarest Cowrie in this region.

Lovely Cowrie
Cypraea pulchra Gray.
5cm/2in. Red Sea & Arabian Coasts. Uncommon.

Teulere's Cowrie
Cypraea teulerei Cazevanette.
5cm/2in. Gulf of Oman (Masirah Island). At one time a great rarity, now common.

Twin-blotched Cowrie
Cypraea nebrites Melvill.
3cm/1.2in. Red Sea to Gulf of Oman. Common.

COWIES OF THE CARIBBEAN, CENTRAL AND SOUTH AMERICA

The Mouse Cowrie comes in three forms; the Atlantic Deer Cowrie (not pictured here) is the largest species, but large shells are now scarce and difficult to obtain.

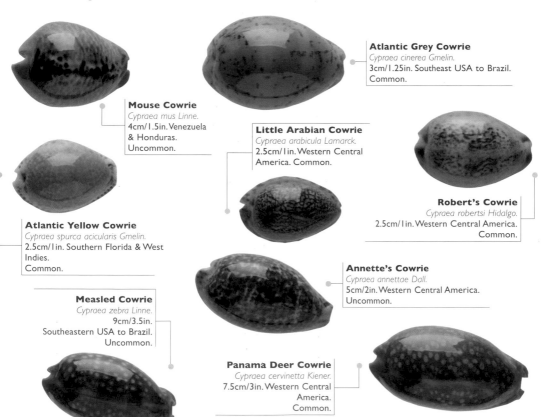

Atlantic Grey Cowrie
Cypraea cinerea Gmelin.
3cm/1.25in. Southeast USA to Brazil.
Common.

Mouse Cowrie
Cypraea mus Linne.
4cm/1.5in. Venezuela
& Honduras.
Uncommon.

Little Arabian Cowrie
Cypraea arabicula Lamarck.
2.5cm/1in. Western Central
America. Common.

Robert's Cowrie
Cypraea robertsi Hidalgo.
2.5cm/1in. Western Central America.
Common.

Atlantic Yellow Cowrie
Cypraea spurca acicularis Gmelin.
2.5cm/1in. Southern Florida & West
Indies.
Common.

Annette's Cowrie
Cypraea annettae Dall.
5cm/2in. Western Central America.
Uncommon.

Measled Cowrie
Cypraea zebra Linne.
9cm/3.5in.
Southeastern USA to Brazil.
Uncommon.

Panama Deer Cowrie
Cypraea cervinetta Kiener.
7.5cm/3in. Western Central
America.
Common.

AUSTRALIAN COWIES

None of these species occur anywhere else in the World. The Zoila group, which includes the Friends, Theresite and Deceptive Cowries are included in this group and inhabit relatively deep waters.

Deceptive Cowrie
Cypraea decipiens E.A. Smith.
5cm/2in. Northwestern Australia.
Uncommon.

Margined Cowrie
Cypraea marginarta Gaskoin.
6cm/2.5in. Western & Southern
Australia.
A shallow- and deep-water rarity.

Plump Cowrie
Cypraea angustata Gmelin.
4cm/1.25in. Southeast Australia
& Tasmania.
Common.

Friend's Cowrie
Cypraea friendii Gray.
10cm/4in. Western & Southwestern Australia.
A well-known shallow and deep-water dweller.
Uncommon.

Thersite Cowrie
Cypraea thersites Gaskoin.
6cm/2.5in. Southern Australia.
Uncommon.

COWIES - THE ARABICA GROUP

Amateur collectors can find these Cowries difficult to distinguish between, as adult markings are similar. Shape, pattern and size must be considered when identifying them. Probably the Histrio and Gray's Cowrie are the most similar.

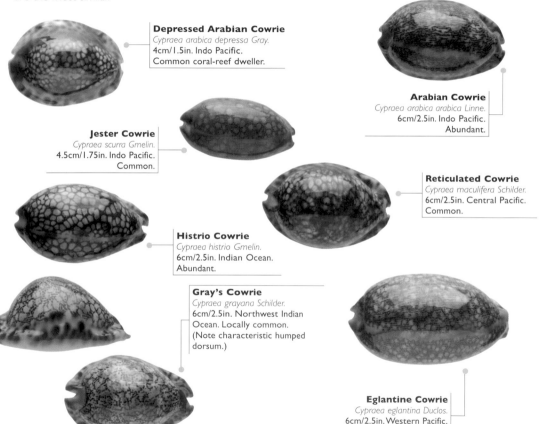

Depressed Arabian Cowrie
Cypraea arabica depressa Gray.
4cm/1.5in. Indo Pacific.
Common coral-reef dweller.

Arabian Cowrie
Cypraea arabica arabica Linne.
6cm/2.5in. Indo Pacific.
Abundant.

Jester Cowrie
Cypraea scurra Gmelin.
4.5cm/1.75in. Indo Pacific.
Common.

Reticulated Cowrie
Cypraea maculifera Schilder.
6cm/2.5in. Central Pacific.
Common.

Histrio Cowrie
Cypraea histrio Gmelin.
6cm/2.5in. Indian Ocean.
Abundant.

Gray's Cowrie
Cypraea grayana Schilder.
6cm/2.5in. Northwest Indian
Ocean. Locally common.
(Note characteristic humped
dorsum.)

Eglantine Cowrie
Cypraea eglantina Duclos.
6cm/2.5in. Western Pacific.
Abundant.

WEST AND SOUTH AFRICAN COWIES

The Cowries of South Africa were for many years difficult to obtain in pristine condition, and many were known only as beached specimens. However, since the late 1970s and the upsurge of scuba diving, the majority of the known South African Cowries has appeared on the market, including the rarer deep-water species.

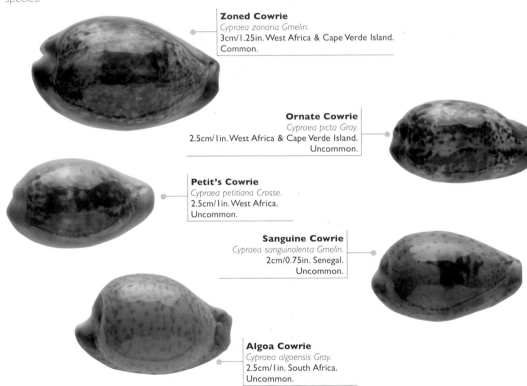

Zoned Cowrie
Cypraea zonaria Gmelin.
3cm/1.25in. West Africa & Cape Verde Island.
Common.

Ornate Cowrie
Cypraea picta Gray.
2.5cm/1in. West Africa & Cape Verde Island.
Uncommon.

Petit's Cowrie
Cypraea petitiana Crosse.
2.5cm/1in. West Africa.
Uncommon.

Sanguine Cowrie
Cypraea sanguinolenta Gmelin.
2cm/0.75in. Senegal.
Uncommon.

Algoa Cowrie
Cypraea algoensis Gray.
2.5cm/1in. South Africa.
Uncommon.

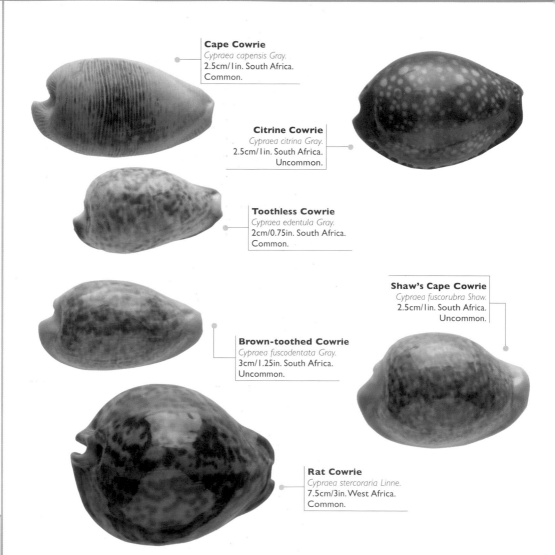

Cape Cowrie
Cypraea capensis Gray.
2.5cm/1in. South Africa.
Common.

Citrine Cowrie
Cypraea citrina Gray.
2.5cm/1in. South Africa.
Uncommon.

Toothless Cowrie
Cypraea edentula Gray.
2cm/0.75in. South Africa.
Common.

Shaw's Cape Cowrie
Cypraea fuscorubra Shaw.
2.5cm/1in. South Africa.
Uncommon.

Brown-toothed Cowrie
Cypraea fuscodentata Gray.
3cm/1.25in. South Africa.
Uncommon.

Rat Cowrie
Cypraea stercoraria Linne.
7.5cm/3in. West Africa.
Common.

COWIES WITH RESTRICTED LOCALITIES

Unlike widespread species, these occur in restricted areas and are thus more difficult to obtain. The Cloudy Cowrie became less of a 'rarity' on the early 1980s. Large showy specimens of the Checkerboard Cowrie command high prices.

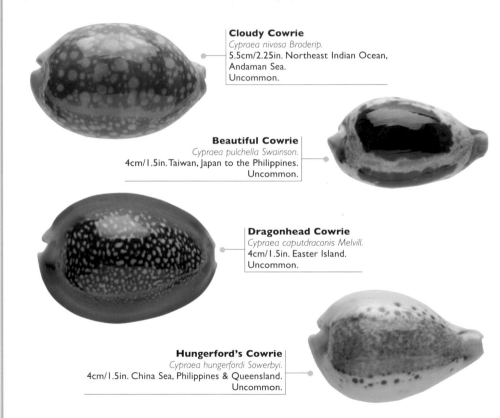

Cloudy Cowrie
Cypraea nivosa Broderip.
5.5cm/2.25in. Northeast Indian Ocean, Andaman Sea.
Uncommon.

Beautiful Cowrie
Cypraea pulchella Swainson.
4cm/1.5in. Taiwan, Japan to the Philippines.
Uncommon.

Dragonhead Cowrie
Cypraea caputdraconis Melvill.
4cm/1.5in. Easter Island.
Uncommon.

Hungerford's Cowrie
Cypraea hungerfordi Sowerbyi.
4cm/1.5in. China Sea, Philippines & Queensland.
Uncommon.

Checkerboard Cowrie
Cypraea tessellata Swainson.
1.5cm/4cm. Hawaiian Islands.
Rare.

Father Englert's Cowrie
Cypraea englerti Summers & Burgess
2.5cm/1in. Easter Island.
Uncommon.

Freckled Cowrie
Cypraea lentiginosa Gray.
3cm/1.25in. India &
Northwestern Indian Ocean.
Uncommon.

Cox's Cowrie
Cypraea coxeni Cox.
3cm/1.25in. New Guinea to Solomon Islands.
Uncommon.

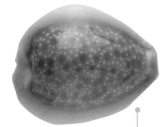

Tahitian Gold-ringed Cowrie
Cypraea annulus obvelata Lamarck.
2cm/0.75in. Tahiti & Marquesas Islands.
Uncommon.

Hawaiian Honey Cowrie
Cypraea helvola hawaiiensis Melvill.
2cm/0.75in. Hawaiian Islands.
Common.

SOME RARE COWIES

At one time, most species shown here were rarely seen in amateur collections. With modern fishing methods, however, they are now available, although some still sell at comparatively high prices.

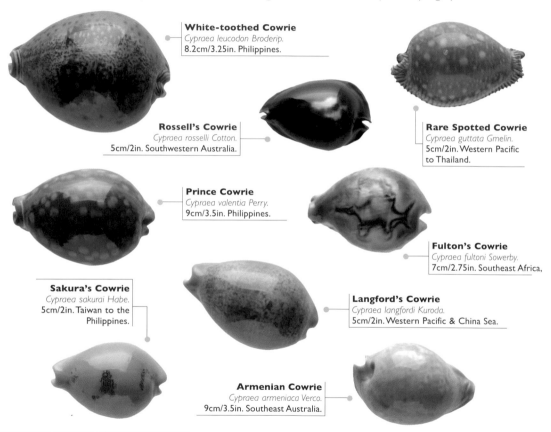

White-toothed Cowrie
Cypraea leucodon Broderip.
8.2cm/3.25in. Philippines.

Rossell's Cowrie
Cypraea rosselli Cotton.
5cm/2in. Southwestern Australia.

Rare Spotted Cowrie
Cypraea guttata Gmelin.
5cm/2in. Western Pacific
to Thailand.

Prince Cowrie
Cypraea valentia Perry.
9cm/3.5in. Philippines.

Fulton's Cowrie
Cypraea fultoni Sowerby.
7cm/2.75in. Southeast Africa,

Sakura's Cowrie
Cypraea sakurai Habe.
5cm/2in. Taiwan to the
Philippines.

Langford's Cowrie
Cypraea langfordi Kuroda.
5cm/2in. Western Pacific & China Sea.

Armenian Cowrie
Cypraea armeniaca Verco.
9cm/3.5in. Southeast Australia.

the golden cowie

This is possibly the most famous, almost legendary and sought-after of all seashells. Greatly prized amongst collectors as well as shell 'fanciers' and lovers of beautiful natural objects.

Cypraea aurantium inhabits deep rocky crevices and caves in depths between 15–45 metres (49–148 feet). It is frequently collected in the Samar Islands (Philippines), and more uncommonly in the Fijian and Solomon Islands.

It has long been a symbol of status and badge of rank among Fijian chiefs, and some specimens have holes bored into them, indicating their use for personal adornment.

Although relatively common in the Philippines, demand for this beautiful and striking shell has always exceeded supply. The price for good specimens has remained fairly constant during the last twenty to thirty years; a fine shell can fetch £100, and a gem, a virtually flawless specimen, perhaps £200.

Unlike some species of Cowries, the Golden Cowrie rarely differs in size or colour. Freshly fished shells are almost magenta in colour, quickly fading to an overall deep orange – the common name aptly describing the enduring impression the shell has on collectors! The majority of shells measure 9–10cm/3.5–4in.

ALLIED COWIES

Although not entirely dissimilar to true Cowries, the Ovulidae (Allied, False or Egg Cowries) are a moderately sized group of species. There are anatomical differences between true and false Cowries and most lack patterns and markings.

They inhabit tropical seas and live in proximity to sponges, sea fans and soft corals. Because of their link to true Cowries, and due to the often-distinctive shape of many species, they promote some interest amongst collectors.

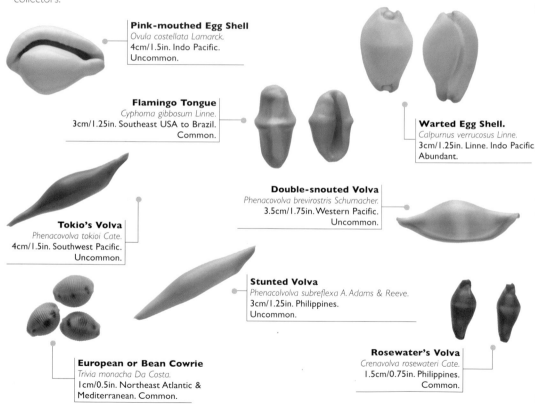

Pink-mouthed Egg Shell
Ovula costellata Lamarck.
4cm/1.5in. Indo Pacific.
Uncommon.

Flamingo Tongue
Cyphoma gibbosum Linne.
3cm/1.25in. Southeast USA to Brazil.
Common.

Warted Egg Shell.
Calpurnus verrucosus Linne.
3cm/1.25in. Linne. Indo Pacific.
Abundant.

Tokio's Volva
Phenacovolva tokioi Cate.
4cm/1.5in. Southwest Pacific.
Uncommon.

Double-snouted Volva
Phenacovolva brevirostris Schumacher.
3.5cm/1.75in. Western Pacific.
Uncommon.

Stunted Volva
Phenacolvolva subreflexa A. Adams & Reeve.
3cm/1.25in. Philippines.
Uncommon.

European or Bean Cowrie
Trivia monacha Da Costa.
1cm/0.5in. Northeast Atlantic &
Mediterranean. Common.

Rosewater's Volva
Crenavolva rosewateri Cate.
1.5cm/0.75in. Philippines.
Common.

MOON OR NECKLACE SNAILS

A large family, the Naticidae are smooth, glossy shells that are carnivorous, feeding on other molluscs. They enjoy worldwide distribution and live mainly on sandy substrates where they dig in search of clams and small snails. There are several genera and they bear differing operculae – both horny and calcareous.

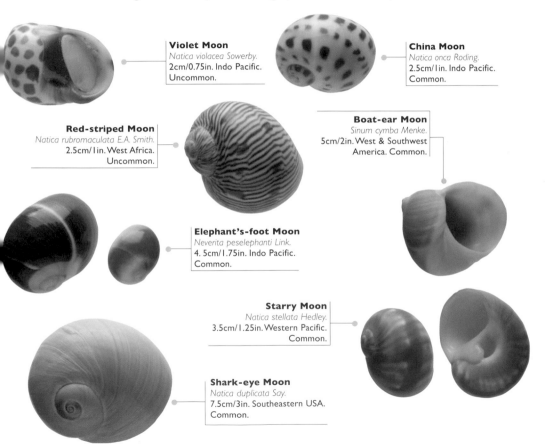

Violet Moon
Natica violacea Sowerby.
2cm/0.75in. Indo Pacific.
Uncommon.

China Moon
Natica onca Roding.
2.5cm/1in. Indo Pacific.
Common.

Red-striped Moon
Natica rubromaculata E.A. Smith.
2.5cm/1in. West Africa.
Uncommon.

Boat-ear Moon
Sinum cymba Menke.
5cm/2in. West & Southwest
America. Common.

Elephant's-foot Moon
Neverita peselephanti Link.
4. 5cm/1.75in. Indo Pacific.
Common.

Starry Moon
Natica stellata Hedley.
3.5cm/1.25in. Western Pacific.
Common.

Shark-eye Moon
Natica duplicata Say.
7.5cm/3in. Southeastern USA.
Common.

Single-banded Moon.
Natica unifasciata Lamarck.
3cm/1.5in. Western Central America.
Common.

Two-banded Moon
Polinices bifasciatus Griffith & Pidgeon.
4cm/1.5in. Western Central America. Common.

Butterfly Moon.
Natica alapapilionis Roding.
4cm/1.5in. Indo Pacific. Common

Golden Moon
Polinices aurantius Roding.
4cm/1.5in. Indo Pacific. Common.

Simiae's Moon
Natica simiae Deshayes.
3cm/1.25in. Western Pacific. Common.

Lined Moon
Natica lineata Roding.
3cm/1.5in. Western Pacific. Common

Colourful Atlantic Moon
Natica canrena
4cm/1.5in. Southeast USA & Caribbean. Common.

Hebrew Moon
Natica maculata Von Salis.
5cm/2in. Mediterranean. Common.

TUN SHELLS

The Tonnidae are a family of large, rounded shells that are generally lightweight. The animal, which is often larger than its shell, is carnivorous, feeding on fish, urchins, crabs and sea cucumbers. They inhabit tropical seas and live in moderate to deep waters.

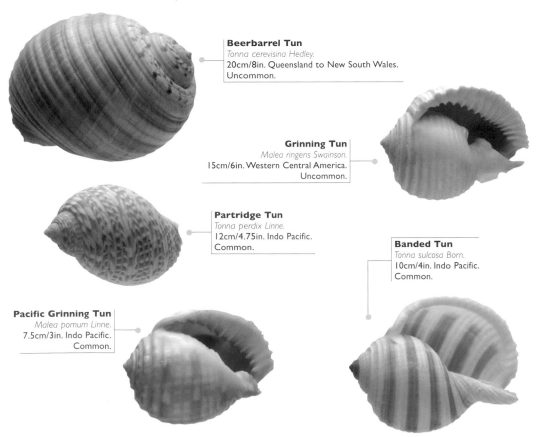

Beerbarrel Tun
Tonna cerevisina Hedley.
20cm/8in. Queensland to New South Wales.
Uncommon.

Grinning Tun
Malea ringens Swainson.
15cm/6in. Western Central America.
Uncommon.

Partridge Tun
Tonna perdix Linne.
12cm/4.75in. Indo Pacific.
Common.

Banded Tun
Tonna sulcosa Born.
10cm/4in. Indo Pacific.
Common.

Pacific Grinning Tun
Malea pomum Linne.
7.5cm/3in. Indo Pacific.
Common.

FIG SHELLS

Fig Shells (Ficidae) live in sand, in tropical seas. They are a small group with thin, lightweight shells.

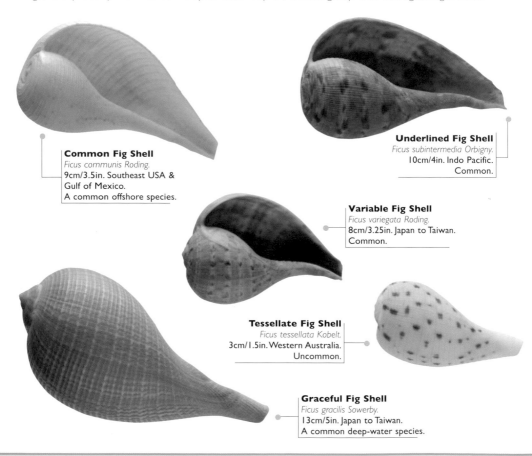

Common Fig Shell
Ficus communis Roding.
9cm/3.5in. Southeast USA &
Gulf of Mexico.
A common offshore species.

Underlined Fig Shell
Ficus subintermedia Orbigny.
10cm/4in. Indo Pacific.
Common.

Variable Fig Shell
Ficus variegata Roding.
8cm/3.25in. Japan to Taiwan.
Common.

Tessellate Fig Shell
Ficus tessellata Kobelt.
3cm/1.5in. Western Australia.
Uncommon.

Graceful Fig Shell
Ficus gracilis Sowerby.
13cm/5in. Japan to Taiwan.
A common deep-water species.

HELMET SHELLS

The Cassidae, known as Helmet or Bonnet shells, are a large family of very solid, often thickened shells found in shallow tropical seas on sand, where they enjoy feeding on sea urchins. The shells here are some of the larger species. The Bullmouth Helmet has long been a popular species in the cameo-jewellery carving industry.

Emperor Helmet
Cassis madagascariensis Lamarck.
18cm/7in. Caribbean.
Uncommon.

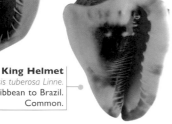

Horned Helmet
Cassis cornuta Linne.
30cm/12in. Indo Pacific.
Common.

Panamanian Bonnet
*Semicassis granulatum
centiquadratum Valenciennes.*
5cm/2in. Western Central
America. Common.

King Helmet
Cassis tuberosa Linne.
15cm/6in. Caribbean to Brazil.
Common.

Flame Helmet
Cassis flammea Linne.
13cm/5in. Florida &
Caribbean. Common.

Reticulated Cowrie-Helmet
Cypraecassis testiculus Linne.
6cm/2.5in. Florida to Brazil.
Common.

Bullmouth Helmet
Cypraecassis rufa Linne.
15cm/6in. East Africa.
Common.

Ihering's Bonnet
Xenopallium labiatum iheringi Carcelles.
6cm/2.5in. Brazil to Argentina.
A rare deep-water species.

Dwarf Helmet
Cassis nana Tenison Woods.
5cm/2in. Eastern Australia.
An uncommon deep-water Helmet.

Banded Helmet
Phalium bandatum Perry.
9cm/3.5in. Western Pacific.
Common.

Vibex Bonnet
Casmaria erinaceus Linne.
5cm/2in. Indo Pacific.
Common.

Rugose Bonnet
Galeodea rugosa Linne.
10cm/4in. Northeast Atlantic &
Mediterranean.
Common.

Fringed Helmet
Cassis fimbriata Quoy & Gaimard
7.5cm/3in. Southern & Western Australia.
Uncommon.

Narrow-mouthed Bonnet
Semicassis microstoma Von Martens.
6cm/2.5in. East Africa to Natal.
A deep-water rarity.

Mediterranean Bonnet
Semicassis granulatum undulatum Gmelin.
9cm/3.5in. Mediterranean.
Common.

TRITON SHELLS

The family Ranellidae boasts many interesting and popular collector's shells, the best known being the Trumpet Triton, which attains a large size and is extremely beautiful in both shape and pattern.
Ranzani's Triton is from a restricted locality and is also a sought-after collector's shell. When alive, the shells are covered by a hairy or bristly periostracum. They are carnivorous and enjoy worldwide distribution.

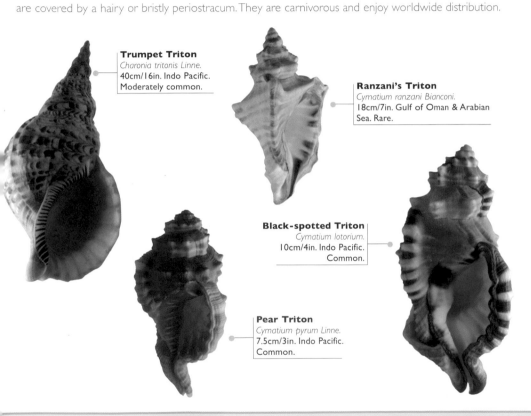

Trumpet Triton
Charonia tritonis Linne.
40cm/16in. Indo Pacific.
Moderately common.

Ranzani's Triton
Cymatium ranzani Bianconi.
18cm/7in. Gulf of Oman & Arabian Sea. Rare.

Black-spotted Triton
Cymatium lotorium.
10cm/4in. Indo Pacific.
Common.

Pear Triton
Cymatium pyrum Linne.
7.5cm/3in. Indo Pacific.
Common.

TRITONS FROM THE CENTRAL AMERICAS

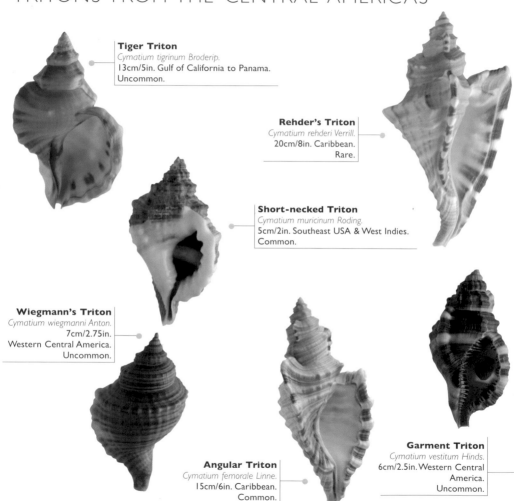

Tiger Triton
Cymatium tigrinum Broderip.
13cm/5in. Gulf of California to Panama.
Uncommon.

Rehder's Triton
Cymatium rehderi Verrill.
20cm/8in. Caribbean.
Rare.

Short-necked Triton
Cymatium muricinum Roding.
5cm/2in. Southeast USA & West Indies.
Common.

Wiegmann's Triton
Cymatium wiegmanni Anton.
7cm/2.75in.
Western Central America.
Uncommon.

Angular Triton
Cymatium femorale Linne.
15cm/6in. Caribbean.
Common.

Garment Triton
Cymatium vestitum Hinds.
6cm/2.5in. Western Central
America.
Uncommon.

SOME WELL-KNOWN INDO-PACIFIC TRITONS

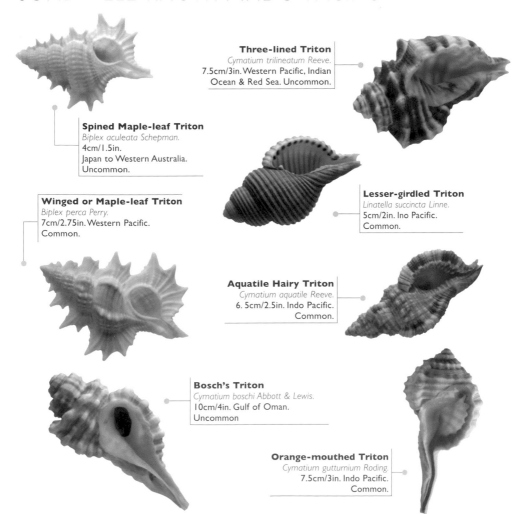

Three-lined Triton
Cymatium trilineatum Reeve.
7.5cm/3in. Western Pacific, Indian
Ocean & Red Sea. Uncommon.

Spined Maple-leaf Triton
Biplex aculeata Schepman.
4cm/1.5in.
Japan to Western Australia.
Uncommon.

Winged or Maple-leaf Triton
Biplex perca Perry.
7cm/2.75in. Western Pacific.
Common.

Lesser-girdled Triton
Linatella succincta Linne.
5cm/2in. Ino Pacific.
Common.

Aquatile Hairy Triton
Cymatium aquatile Reeve.
6. 5cm/2.5in. Indo Pacific.
Common.

Bosch's Triton
Cymatium boschi Abbott & Lewis.
10cm/4in. Gulf of Oman.
Uncommon

Orange-mouthed Triton
Cymatium gutturnium Roding.
7.5cm/3in. Indo Pacific.
Common.

AUSTRALIAN TRITONS

Australian Brown Triton
Ranella australasia Perry.
10cm/4in. New South Wales
to Western Australia.
Common.

Distorted Rock Triton
Sassia subdistorta Lamarck.
5cm/2in. Southern Australia & Tasmania.
Common.

Powell's Triton
Charonia rubicunda powelli Cotton.
15cm/6in. South Australia.
Uncommon.

Neopolitan Triton
Cymatium parthenopeum Von Salis.
10cm/4in. A very widespread
species; Australia & worldwide
tropical seas.
Common.

Spengler's Triton
Cabestana spengleri Perry.
10cm/4in. South Australia & Tasmania.
Common.

INDO-PACIFIC TRITONS

Tadpole Triton
Gyrineum gyrinum Linne.
2.5cm/1in.
Common.

Kurz's Distorsio
Distorsio kurzi Petuch & Harasewych.
4cm/1.5in. Deep water.
Uncommon.

Bent-neck Triton
Cymatium caudatum Gmelin.
9cm/3.5in.
Common.

Robin Redbreast Triton
Cymatium rubeculum Linne.
4cm/1.5in.
Common.

Black-striped Triton
Cymatium hepaticum Roding.
5cm/2in.
Common.

Common Distorsio
Distorsio anus Linne.
7cm/2.75in.
Common.

FROG SHELLS FROM THE INDO PACIFIC

The Bursidae are closely related to the Tritons. Small or medium-sized species, they mostly live in warm, shallow water, under rocks or in corals, feeding on marine worms.

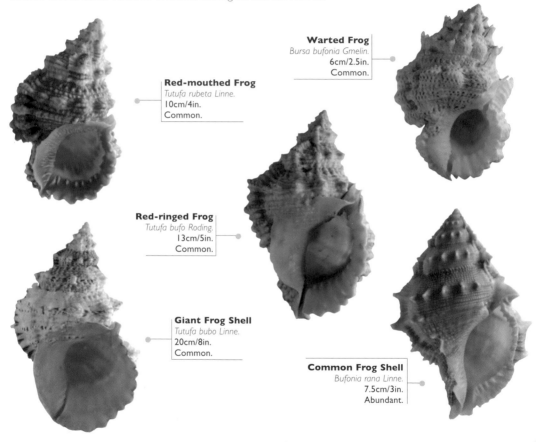

Red-mouthed Frog
Tutufa rubeta Linne.
10cm/4in.
Common.

Warted Frog
Bursa bufonia Gmelin.
6cm/2.5in.
Common.

Red-ringed Frog
Tutufa bufo Roding.
13cm/5in.
Common.

Giant Frog Shell
Tutufa bubo Linne.
20cm/8in.
Common.

Common Frog Shell
Bufonia rana Linne.
7.5cm/3in.
Abundant.

AMERICAN FROG SHELLS

Chestnut Frog
Bufonaria bufo Bruguiere.
5cm/2in. Florida to Brazil.
Uncommon.

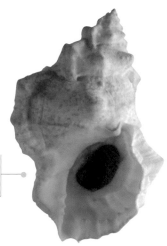

Californian Frog
Crossata californica Hinds.
15cm/6in. California to West Mexico.
Uncommon.

Gaudy Frog Shell
Bursa corrugata Perry.
5cm/2in. Caribbean & Tropical
Central America.
Uncommon.

Granulate Frog
Bursa granularis Roding.
7cm/2.75in. Caribbean & Indo Pacific.
Common.

WENTLETRAPS

The Epitoniidae are a family of collector's favourites comprising over 200 species of exquisitely ornamented and sculptured shells, some very rare. They live amongst and feed on sea anemones and soft corals. Many species inhabit deep water and lack colour, being white or cream. The name 'Wentletrap' derives from a German word meaning 'spiral staircase'.

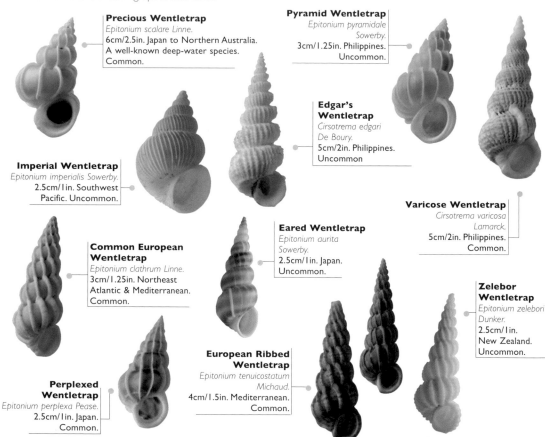

Precious Wentletrap
Epitonium scalare Linne.
6cm/2.5in. Japan to Northern Australia.
A well-known deep-water species.
Common.

Pyramid Wentletrap
*Epitonium pyramidale
Sowerby.*
3cm/1.25in. Philippines.
Uncommon.

**Edgar's
Wentletrap**
*Cirsotrema edgari
De Boury.*
5cm/2in. Philippines.
Uncommon

Imperial Wentletrap
Epitonium imperialis Sowerby.
2.5cm/1in. Southwest
Pacific. Uncommon.

Varicose Wentletrap
*Cirsotrema varicosa
Lamarck.*
5cm/2in. Philippines.
Common.

**Common European
Wentletrap**
Epitonium clathrum Linne.
3cm/1.25in. Northeast
Atlantic & Mediterranean.
Common.

Eared Wentletrap
*Epitonium aurita
Sowerby.*
2.5cm/1in. Japan.
Uncommon.

**Zelebor
Wentletrap**
*Epitonium zelebori
Dunker.*
2.5cm/1in.
New Zealand.
Uncommon.

**Perplexed
Wentletrap**
Epitonium perplexa Pease.
2.5cm/1in. Japan.
Common.

**European Ribbed
Wentletrap**
*Epitonium tenuicostatum
Michaud.*
4cm/1.5in. Mediterranean.
Common.

PURPLE SEA SNAILS

Janthinidae occupy a unique place amongst molluscs. They are thin, fragile shells that live pelagic lives – they are borne along on the surface of warm seas on a 'raft' of mucous-covered bubbles to which they are attached, inverted, by their foot. There are only about ten known species. After storms, many are found washed up on beaches in worldwide locations, but few are found intact. They feed on floating organisms such as small jellyfish and molluscan larvae.

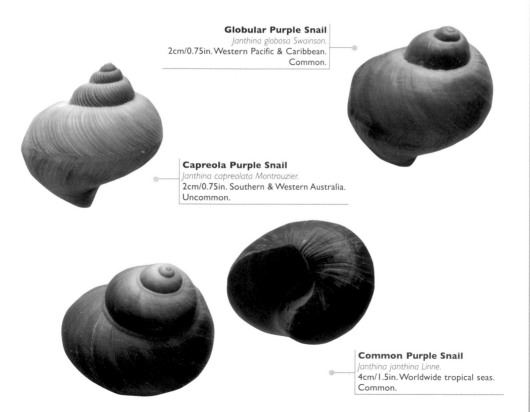

Globular Purple Snail
Janthina globosa Swainson.
2cm/0.75in. Western Pacific & Caribbean.
Common.

Capreola Purple Snail
Janthina capreolata Montrouzier.
2cm/0.75in. Southern & Western Australia.
Uncommon.

Common Purple Snail
Janthina janthina Linne.
4cm/1.5in. Worldwide tropical seas.
Common.

SPINY MUREX SHELLS

The Muricidae, also known as Rock Shells, is a very large family of molluscs numbering in excess of 1,000 species. The spiny shells shown here are in the genus Murex. The Venus Comb is a collector's favourite – often fished with all spines intact!

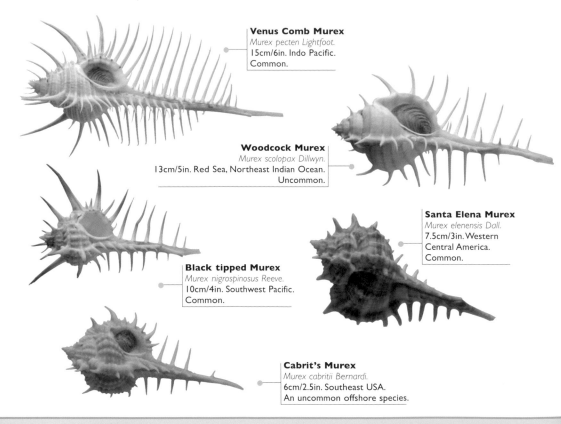

Venus Comb Murex
Murex pecten Lightfoot.
15cm/6in. Indo Pacific.
Common.

Woodcock Murex
Murex scolopax Dillwyn.
13cm/5in. Red Sea, Northeast Indian Ocean.
Uncommon.

Santa Elena Murex
Murex elenensis Dall.
7.5cm/3in. Western
Central America.
Common.

Black tipped Murex
Murex nigrospinosus Reeve.
10cm/4in. Southwest Pacific.
Common.

Cabrit's Murex
Murex cabritii Bernardi.
6cm/2.5in. Southeast USA.
An uncommon offshore species.

MUREX SHELLS

A selection from the popular genus Chicoreus, the Rose-branched Murex being a long-standing favourite. This species requires much painstaking time spent cleaning off marine encrustations, etc. The Endive Murex varies in both colour and spines.

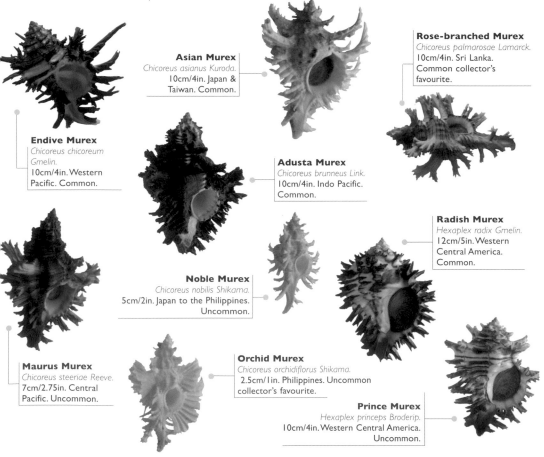

Asian Murex
Chicoreus asianus Kuroda.
10cm/4in. Japan &
Taiwan. Common.

Rose-branched Murex
Chicoreus palmarosae Lamarck.
10cm/4in. Sri Lanka.
Common collector's
favourite.

Endive Murex
*Chicoreus chicoreum
Gmelin.*
10cm/4in. Western
Pacific. Common.

Adusta Murex
Chicoreus brunneus Link.
10cm/4in. Indo Pacific.
Common.

Radish Murex
Hexaplex radix Gmelin.
12cm/5in. Western
Central America.
Common.

Noble Murex
Chicoreus nobilis Shikama.
5cm/2in. Japan to the Philippines.
Uncommon.

Maurus Murex
Chicoreus steeriae Reeve.
7cm/2.75in. Central
Pacific. Uncommon.

Orchid Murex
Chicoreus orchidiflorus Shikama.
2.5cm/1in. Philippines. Uncommon
collector's favourite.

Prince Murex
Hexaplex princeps Broderip.
10cm/4in. Western Central America.
Uncommon.

MUREX SHELLS

As with all species in the Muricidae, it is important to collectors that all or most spines are intact where possible.

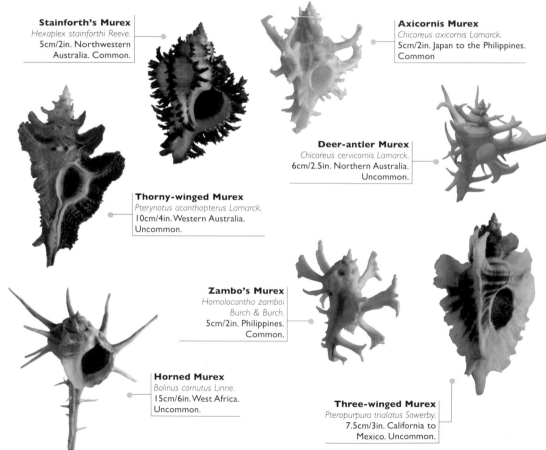

Stainforth's Murex
Hexaplex stainforthi Reeve.
5cm/2in. Northwestern
Australia. Common.

Axicornis Murex
Chicoreus axicornis Lamarck.
5cm/2in. Japan to the Philippines.
Common

Deer-antler Murex
Chicoreus cervicornis Lamarck.
6cm/2.5in. Northern Australia.
Uncommon.

Thorny-winged Murex
Pterynotus acanthopterus Lamarck.
10cm/4in. Western Australia.
Uncommon.

Zambo's Murex
*Homolocantha zamboi
Burch & Burch.*
5cm/2in. Philippines.
Common.

Horned Murex
Bolinus cornutus Linne.
15cm/6in. West Africa.
Uncommon.

Three-winged Murex
Pteropurpura trialatus Sowerby.
7.5cm/3in. California to
Mexico. Uncommon.

MUREX SHELLS

The Alabaster Murex was once a great rarity, the earliest specimen known was found in 1836–39, in the Philippines, by Hugh Cumming. It was not until almost 125 years later that the species was collected again; it is now relatively common.

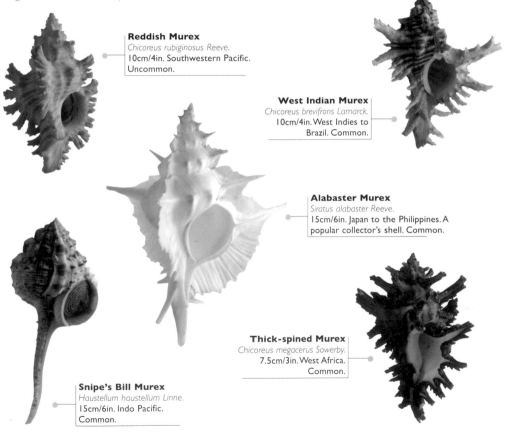

Reddish Murex
Chicoreus rubiginosus Reeve.
10cm/4in. Southwestern Pacific. Uncommon.

West Indian Murex
Chicoreus brevifrons Lamarck.
10cm/4in. West Indies to Brazil. Common.

Alabaster Murex
Siratus alabaster Reeve.
15cm/6in. Japan to the Philippines. A popular collector's shell. Common.

Thick-spined Murex
Chicoreus megacerus Sowerby.
7.5cm/3in. West Africa. Common.

Snipe's Bill Murex
Haustellum haustellum Linne.
15cm/6in. Indo Pacific. Common.

the dye murex

Both species shown here were widely used in the days of the Phoenicians, Greeks and Romans for the manufacture of purple dye. When boiled, the snail secretes a yellowish fluid, which turns a deep purple when placed in direct sunlight.

It is known that many thousands of such shells were needed to produce only a small amount of this precious fluid. The dye commanded very high prices and was only available to nobility and the rich; it was used to dye imperial robes and ecclesiastical garments.

During Roman times, only senators and emperors were allowed to wear purple robes, and, after the fall of the western empire, the dye was used by the Christian Church and gave rise to the official colour of cardinal's robes.

During the height of dye-producing by the Phoenicians, many new towns and cities grew up along Mediterranean coasts as fishermen sought new Dye Murex beds.

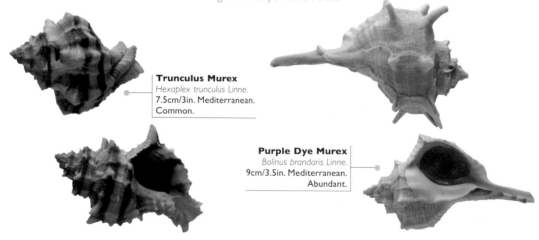

Trunculus Murex
Hexaplex trunculus Linne.
7.5cm/3in. Mediterranean.
Common.

Purple Dye Murex
Bolinus brandaris Linne.
9cm/3.5in. Mediterranean.
Abundant.

UNCOMMON AND RARE MUREX

These species are keenly sought after by amateur collectors and can command high prices.

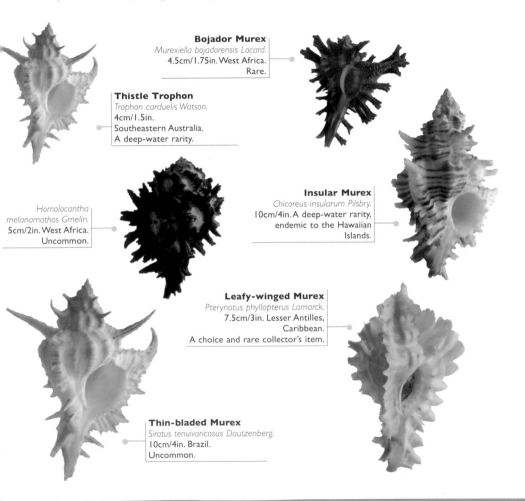

Bojador Murex
Murexiella bojadorensis Locard.
4.5cm/1.75in. West Africa.
Rare.

Thistle Trophon
Trophon carduelis Watson.
4cm/1.5in.
Southeastern Australia.
A deep-water rarity.

*Homolocantha
melanamathos Gmelin.*
5cm/2in. West Africa.
Uncommon.

Insular Murex
Chicoreus insularum Pilsbry.
10cm/4in. A deep-water rarity,
endemic to the Hawaiian
Islands.

Leafy-winged Murex
Pterynotus phyllopterus Lamarck.
7.5cm/3in. Lesser Antilles,
Caribbean.
A choice and rare collector's item.

Thin-bladed Murex
Siratus tenuivaricosus Dautzenberg.
10cm/4in. Brazil.
Uncommon.

DRUPE SNAILS

The Drupes are a small, colourful group found on the coral-rock shores of the Indo-Pacific region. They are placed in the Muricidae sub-family, Thaidinae.

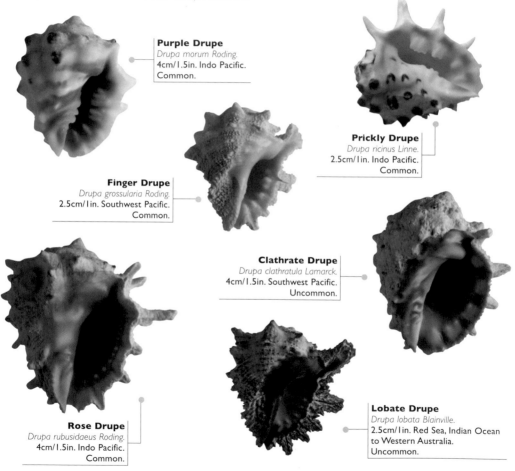

Purple Drupe
Drupa morum Roding.
4cm/1.5in. Indo Pacific.
Common.

Prickly Drupe
Drupa ricinus Linne.
2.5cm/1in. Indo Pacific.
Common.

Finger Drupe
Drupa grossularia Roding.
2.5cm/1in. Southwest Pacific.
Common.

Clathrate Drupe
Drupa clathratula Lamarck.
4cm/1.5in. Southwest Pacific.
Uncommon.

Rose Drupe
Drupa rubusidaeus Roding.
4cm/1.5in. Indo Pacific.
Common.

Lobate Drupe
Drupa lobata Blainville.
2.5cm/1in. Red Sea, Indian Ocean
to Western Australia.
Uncommon.

ROCK SHELLS

All Thaids live in colonies on rocky shores where they feed on oysters, barnacles and mussels. The Atlantic Dog Whelk is found in large numbers on rocks living amongst Mussel colonies on which they feed. They occur in a wide range of pastel colours.

Rudolph's Purpura
Purpura panama Roding.
7.5cm/3in. East Indies.
A common shallow-water dweller.

Persian Purpura
Purpura persica Linne.
6cm/2.5in. Southwest Pacific.
A common species found
on inter-tidal rocks.

Wide-mouthed Purpura
Purpura patula Linne.
6cm/2.5in. Florida & West Indies.
Common well-known shell.

Tuberose Rock Shell
Thais tuberosa Roding.
5cm/2in. Southwest Pacific.
Common.

Bezoar Rapa Whelk
Rapana bezoar Linne.
7cm/2.75in. Japan to Taiwan.
Common.

Girdled Rock Shell
Thais cingulata Linne.
5cm/2in. South Africa.
Uncommon.

Atlantic Dog Whelk
Nucella lapillus Linne.
4cm/1.5in. Northwest &
Northeast Atlantic coasts.
Abundant.

Gourd Rock Shell
Thais melones Duclos.
4cm/1.5in. Western Central
America & Galapagos Islands.
Common.

Thomas's Rapa Whelk
Rapana venosa Valenciennes.
15cm/6in. Japan, China & Black Sea.
A large predatory species. Common.

LATIAXIS SHELLS

The Coralliophilidae are a beautiful family of delicately sculptured shells living mostly in deeper waters. Although they are related to the Murex shells they are parasitic and many species do not have radula teeth. They live amongst soft and hard corals. Popular with collectors.

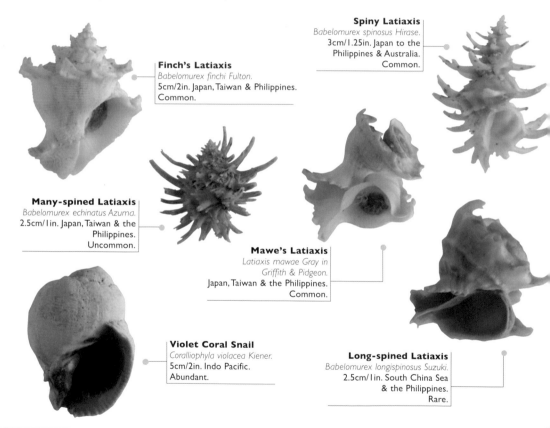

Spiny Latiaxis
Babelomurex spinosus Hirase.
3cm/1.25in. Japan to the
Philippines & Australia.
Common.

Finch's Latiaxis
Babelomurex finchi Fulton.
5cm/2in. Japan, Taiwan & Philippines.
Common.

Many-spined Latiaxis
Babelomurex echinatus Azuma.
2.5cm/1in. Japan, Taiwan & the
Philippines.
Uncommon.

Mawe's Latiaxis
*Latiaxis mawae Gray in
Griffith & Pidgeon.*
Japan, Taiwan & the Philippines.
Common.

Violet Coral Snail
Coralliophyla violacea Kiener.
5cm/2in. Indo Pacific.
Abundant.

Long-spined Latiaxis
Babelomurex longispinosus Suzuki.
2.5cm/1in. South China Sea
& the Philippines.
Rare.

LATIAXIS SHELLS

The Bubble Turnip shell lives in the soft, yellow sea-fan corals of the Philippines. It is also known as the Papery Rapa Snail.

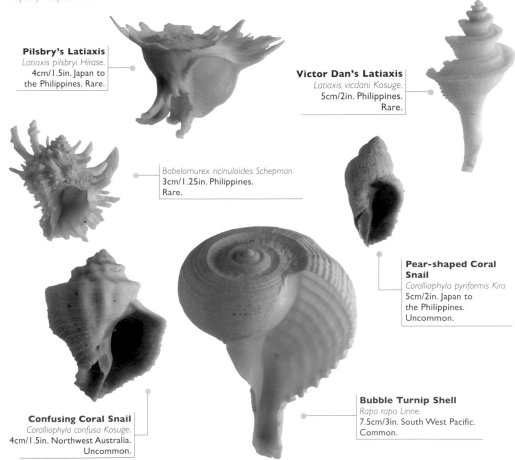

Pilsbry's Latiaxis
Latiaxis pilsbryi Hirase.
4cm/1.5in. Japan to
the Philippines. Rare.

Victor Dan's Latiaxis
Latiaxis vicdani Kosuge.
5cm/2in. Philippines.
Rare.

Babelomurex ricinuloides Schepman.
3cm/1.25in. Philippines.
Rare.

Pear-shaped Coral Snail
Coralliophyla pyriformis Kira
5cm/2in. Japan to
the Philippines.
Uncommon.

Confusing Coral Snail
Coralliophyla confusa Kosuge.
4cm/1.5in. Northwest Australia.
Uncommon.

Bubble Turnip Shell
Rapa rapa Linne.
7.5cm/3in. South West Pacific.
Common.

BABYLON WHELKS

A large and diverse family of over 400 species, the Buccinidae comprises numerous genera. All Whelks are carnivorous and inhabit both cold polar and tropical seas, feeding on echinoids, Bivalves and marine worms. The cooler, often deep-water species tend to be drab and dull in appearance, whereas tropical species are patterned and colourful.

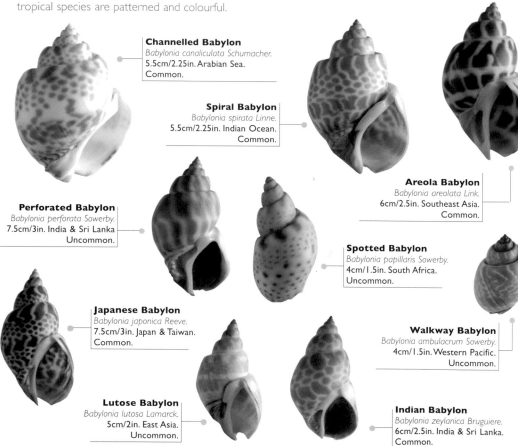

Channelled Babylon
Babylonia canaliculata Schumacher.
5.5cm/2.25in. Arabian Sea.
Common.

Spiral Babylon
Babylonia spirata Linne.
5.5cm/2.25in. Indian Ocean.
Common.

Areola Babylon
Babylonia areolata Link.
6cm/2.5in. Southeast Asia.
Common.

Perforated Babylon
Babylonia perforata Sowerby.
7.5cm/3in. India & Sri Lanka.
Uncommon.

Spotted Babylon
Babylonia papillaris Sowerby.
4cm/1.5in. South Africa.
Uncommon.

Japanese Babylon
Babylonia japonica Reeve.
7.5cm/3in. Japan & Taiwan.
Common.

Walkway Babylon
Babylonia ambulacrum Sowerby.
4cm/1.5in. Western Pacific.
Uncommon.

Lutose Babylon
Babylonia lutosa Lamarck.
5cm/2in. East Asia.
Uncommon.

Indian Babylon
Babylonia zeylanica Bruguiere.
6cm/2.5in. India & Sri Lanka.
Common.

WHELK SHELLS

These common species are often popular seafood shells.

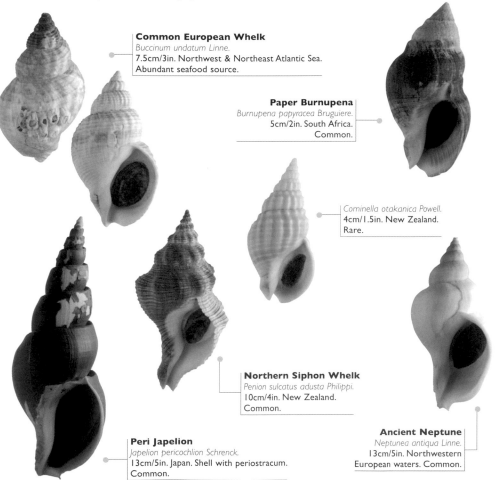

Common European Whelk
Buccinum undatum Linne.
7.5cm/3in. Northwest & Northeast Atlantic Sea.
Abundant seafood source.

Paper Burnupena
Burnupena papyracea Bruguiere.
5cm/2in. South Africa.
Common.

Cominella otakanica Powell.
4cm/1.5in. New Zealand.
Rare.

Northern Siphon Whelk
Penion sulcatus adusta Philippi.
10cm/4in. New Zealand.
Common.

Peri Japelion
Japelion pericochlion Schrenck.
13cm/5in. Japan. Shell with periostracum.
Common.

Ancient Neptune
Neptunea antiqua Linne.
13cm/5in. Northwestern
European waters. Common.

UNCOMMON AND RARE WHELKS

Many rare Whelks inhabit the cooler, deeper waters of the Northern Hemisphere and are occasionally taken by trawling fishing boats.

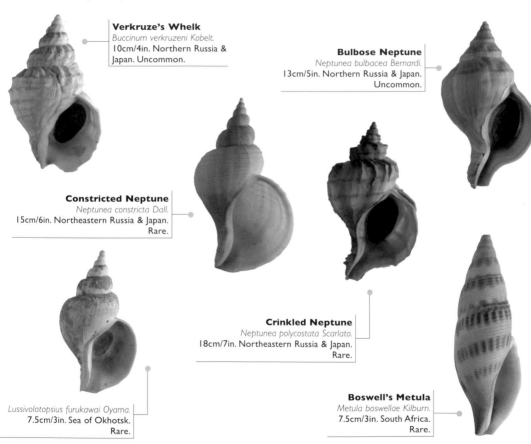

Verkruze's Whelk
Buccinum verkruzeni Kobelt.
10cm/4in. Northern Russia & Japan. Uncommon.

Bulbose Neptune
Neptunea bulbacea Bernardi.
13cm/5in. Northern Russia & Japan.
Uncommon.

Constricted Neptune
Neptunea constricta Dall.
15cm/6in. Northeastern Russia & Japan.
Rare.

Crinkled Neptune
Neptunea polycostata Scarlato.
18cm/7in. Northeastern Russia & Japan.
Rare.

Lussivolotopsius furukawai Oyama.
7.5cm/3in. Sea of Okhotsk.
Rare.

Boswell's Metula
Metula boswellae Kilburn.
7.5cm/3in. South Africa.
Rare.

DOVE SHELLS

The Columbellidae number in excess of 400 relatively small species. They have smooth, patterned shells and live in warm waters. They are carnivorous, night-feeding scavengers.

Common Dove Shell
Columbella mercatoria Linne.
2cm/0.75in. Caribbean,
Florida to Brazil.
Abundant.

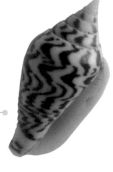

Punctate Dove Shell
Pyrene punctata Bruguiere.
2cm/0.75in. Indo Pacific.
Uncommon.

Philippine Dove Shell
Pyrene epamella Duclos.
2.5cm/1in. Southwest Pacific.
Uncommon.

Yellow Dove Shell
Pyrene flava Bruguiere.
2.5cm/1in. Indo Pacific.
Common.

Stromboid Dove Shell
Columbella strombiformis Lamarck.
2.5cm/1in. Western Central America.
Common.

Lightning Dove Shell
Pyrene ocellata Link.
2cm/0.75in. Indo Pacific.
Common.

DOG WHELKS OR NASSA MUD SNAILS

Another large family of mainly small shells, the Nassariidae inhabit shallow inter-tidal waters in muddy substrates. They are carnivorous scavengers and live in large colonies.

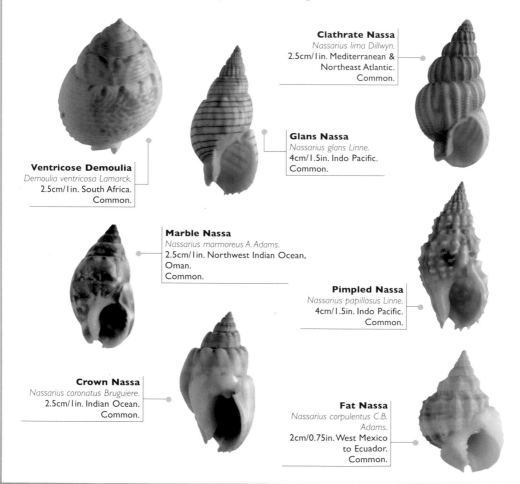

Clathrate Nassa
Nassarius lima Dillwyn.
2.5cm/1in. Mediterranean &
Northeast Atlantic.
Common.

Glans Nassa
Nassarius glans Linne.
4cm/1.5in. Indo Pacific.
Common.

Ventricose Demoulia
Demoulia ventricosa Lamarck.
2.5cm/1in. South Africa.
Common.

Marble Nassa
Nassarius marmoreus A. Adams.
2.5cm/1in. Northwest Indian Ocean,
Oman.
Common.

Pimpled Nassa
Nassarius papillosus Linne.
4cm/1.5in. Indo Pacific.
Common.

Crown Nassa
Nassarius coronatus Bruguiere.
2.5cm/1in. Indian Ocean.
Common.

Fat Nassa
*Nassarius corpulentus C.B.
Adams.*
2cm/0.75in. West Mexico
to Ecuador.
Common.

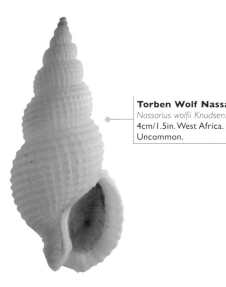

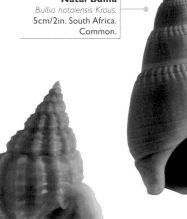

Torben Wolf Nassa
Nassarius wolfii Knudsen.
4cm/1.5in. West Africa.
Uncommon.

Natal Bullia
Bullia natalensis Kraus.
5cm/2in. South Africa.
Common.

Angolan Nassa
Nassarius pachychilus Maltzan.
2cm/0.75in. West Africa.
Uncommon.

Red-banded Nassa
Nassarius pyrrhus Menke.
2cm/0.75in. South Australia & New Zealand.
Common.

Conoidal Nassa
Nassarius conoidalis Deshayes in Belanger.
2cm/0.75in. Indian Ocean.
Common.

SWAMP CONCH (BUSYCON WHELKS)

These shells are in the family Melongenidae. The Lighting Whelk is naturally sinistral (left-handed or reversed coiling).

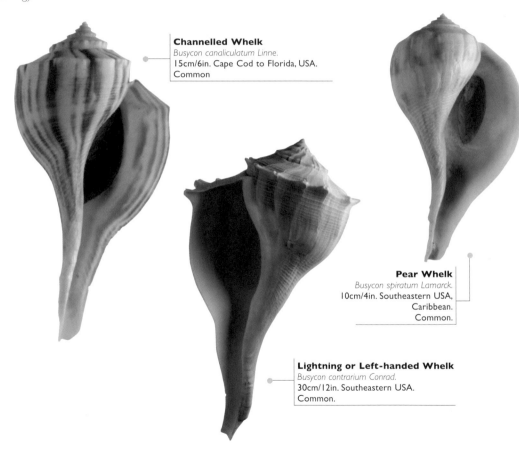

Channelled Whelk
Busycon canaliculatum Linne.
15cm/6in. Cape Cod to Florida, USA.
Common

Pear Whelk
Busycon spiratum Lamarck.
10cm/4in. Southeastern USA,
Caribbean.
Common.

Lightning or Left-handed Whelk
Busycon contrarium Conrad.
30cm/12in. Southeastern USA.
Common.

MELON AND CROWN CONCH

The Florida Crown Conch can vary in size, sculpture and colouration. Large, intact specimens are scarce and popular with collectors.

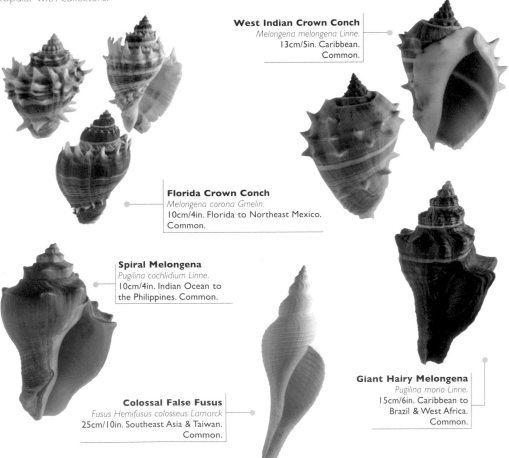

West Indian Crown Conch
Melongena melongena Linne.
13cm/5in. Caribbean.
Common.

Florida Crown Conch
Melongena corona Gmelin.
10cm/4in. Florida to Northeast Mexico.
Common.

Spiral Melongena
Pugilina cochlidium Linne.
10cm/4in. Indian Ocean to
the Philippines. Common.

Colossal False Fusus
Fusus Hemifusus colosseus Lamarck
25cm/10in. Southeast Asia & Taiwan.
Common.

Giant Hairy Melongena
Pugilina morio Linne.
15cm/6in. Caribbean to
Brazil & West Africa.
Common.

australian or false trumpet

Syrinx aruanus Linne is the largest Gastropod shell in existence, measuring up to 60cm/24in. It occurs in the warm waters off the tip of Northern Australia and has in past times been used by natives for ceremonial and domestic purposes. When fresh, it is covered by a thick, brown coarse periostracum, and, when cleaned off, reveals a delicate peach-orange colouration. Immature shells have an unusually long protoconch with many whorls; this is eroded as the shell grows and is completely absent in adult shells. A large specimen is a stunning addition to any collection. The small, immature shell clearly shows the elongated protoconch.

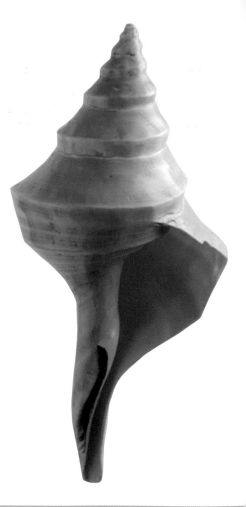

TULIP SHELLS

Tulip Shells, or Fasciolariidae, are a large and popular group of medium and large shells. Most species live in warm tropical waters and are carnivorous, feeding on other molluscs.

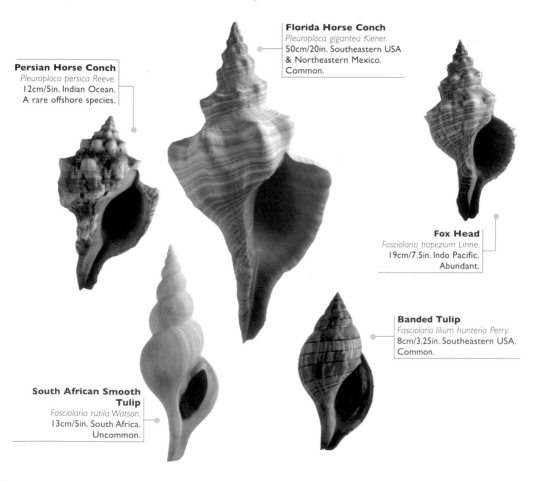

Florida Horse Conch
Pleuroploca gigantea Kiener.
50cm/20in. Southeastern USA
& Northeastern Mexico.
Common.

Persian Horse Conch
Pleuroploca persica Reeve.
12cm/5in. Indian Ocean.
A rare offshore species.

Fox Head
Fasciolaria trapezium Linne.
19cm/7.5in. Indo Pacific.
Abundant.

Banded Tulip
Fasciolaria lilium hunteria Perry.
8cm/3.25in. Southeastern USA.
Common.

**South African Smooth
Tulip**
Fasciolaria rutila Watson.
13cm/5in. South Africa.
Uncommon.

SPINDLE SHELLS

These are elegant shells with tall spires and long siphonal canals. The Cyrtulus Spindle is a difficult to obtain collector's favourite.

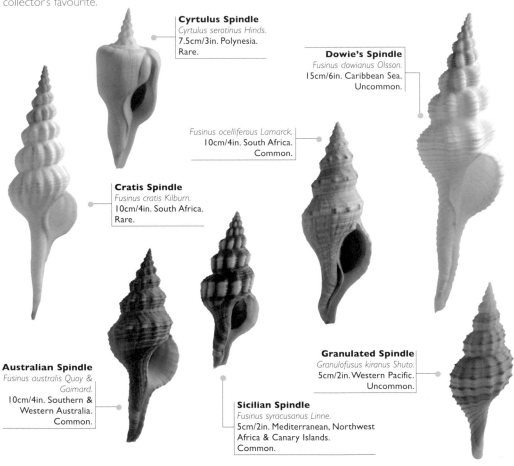

Cyrtulus Spindle
Cyrtulus serotinus Hinds.
7.5cm/3in. Polynesia.
Rare.

Dowie's Spindle
Fusinus dowianus Olsson.
15cm/6in. Caribbean Sea.
Uncommon.

Fusinus ocelliferous Lamarck.
10cm/4in. South Africa.
Common.

Cratis Spindle
Fusinus cratis Kilburn.
10cm/4in. South Africa.
Rare.

Australian Spindle
Fusinus australis Quoy &
Gaimard.
10cm/4in. Southern &
Western Australia.
Common.

Sicilian Spindle
Fusinus syracusanus Linne.
5cm/2in. Mediterranean, Northwest
Africa & Canary Islands.
Common.

Granulated Spindle
Granulofusus kiranus Shuto.
5cm/2in. Western Pacific.
Uncommon.

LATIRUS SHELLS

Also in the Fasciolariidae), these solid shells display a wide range of sculpturing, ornamentation and colour.
They mostly live in warm seas in both shallow and deeper water.

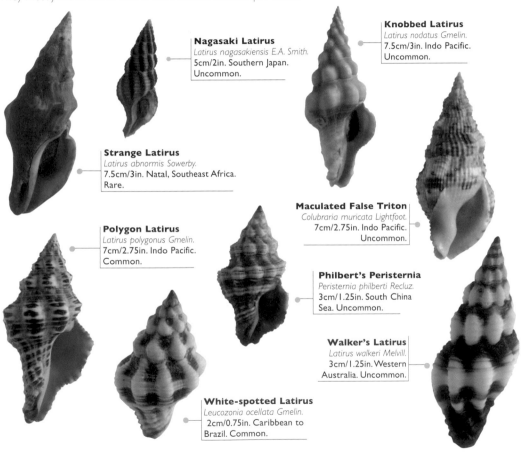

Knobbed Latirus
Latirus nodatus Gmelin.
7.5cm/3in. Indo Pacific.
Uncommon.

Nagasaki Latirus
Latirus nagasakiensis E.A. Smith.
5cm/2in. Southern Japan.
Uncommon.

Strange Latirus
Latirus abnormis Sowerby.
7.5cm/3in. Natal, Southeast Africa.
Rare.

Maculated False Triton
Colubraria muricata Lightfoot.
7cm/2.75in. Indo Pacific.
Uncommon.

Polygon Latirus
Latirus polygonus Gmelin.
7cm/2.75in. Indo Pacific.
Common.

Philbert's Peristernia
Peristernia philberti Recluz.
3cm/1.25in. South China
Sea. Uncommon.

Walker's Latirus
Latirus walkeri Melvill.
3cm/1.25in. Western
Australia. Uncommon.

White-spotted Latirus
Leucozonia ocellata Gmelin.
2cm/0.75in. Caribbean to
Brazil. Common.

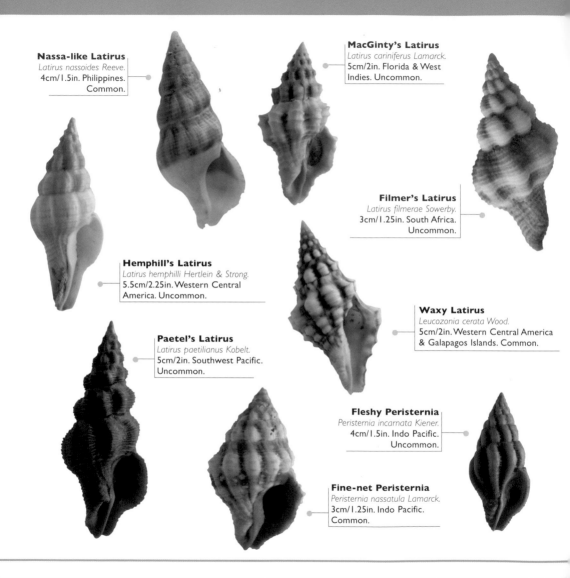

Nassa-like Latirus
Latirus nassoides Reeve.
4cm/1.5in. Philippines.
Common.

MacGinty's Latirus
Latirus cariniferus Lamarck.
5cm/2in. Florida & West
Indies. Uncommon.

Filmer's Latirus
Latirus filmerae Sowerby.
3cm/1.25in. South Africa.
Uncommon.

Hemphill's Latirus
Latirus hemphilli Hertlein & Strong.
5.5cm/2.25in. Western Central
America. Uncommon.

Waxy Latirus
Leucozonia cerata Wood.
5cm/2in. Western Central America
& Galapagos Islands. Common.

Paetel's Latirus
Latirus paetilianus Kobelt.
5cm/2in. Southwest Pacific.
Uncommon.

Fleshy Peristernia
Peristernia incarnata Kiener.
4cm/1.5in. Indo Pacific.
Uncommon.

Fine-net Peristernia
Peristernia nassatula Lamarck.
3cm/1.25in. Indo Pacific.
Common.

VOLUTE SHELLS

A large and well-known family, the Volutidae are very popular with collectors, possibly due to the wide variety of patterns and colours the shells display.

There are numerous genera. They occupy worldwide seas, but the warmer-water species are the more colourful and attractive. Many·are rare deep-water shells and are much sought after.

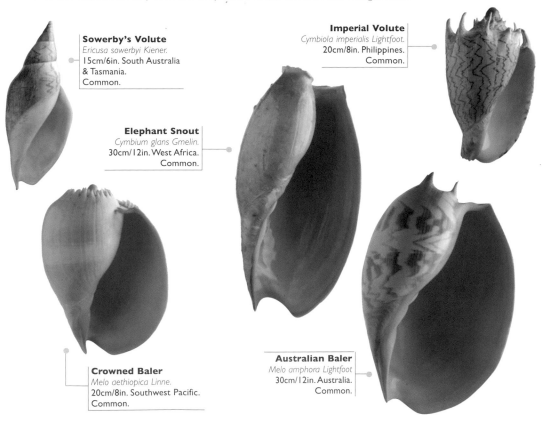

Sowerby's Volute
Ericusa sowerbyi Kiener.
15cm/6in. South Australia & Tasmania.
Common.

Imperial Volute
Cymbiola imperialis Lightfoot.
20cm/8in. Philippines.
Common.

Elephant Snout
Cymbium glans Gmelin.
30cm/12in. West Africa.
Common.

Crowned Baler
Melo aethiopica Linne.
20cm/8in. Southwest Pacific.
Common.

Australian Baler
Melo amphora Lightfoot
30cm/12in. Australia.
Common.

COLD-WATER VOLUTES

These shells are lacking the high gloss and vibrant colours of the shallow warm water species.

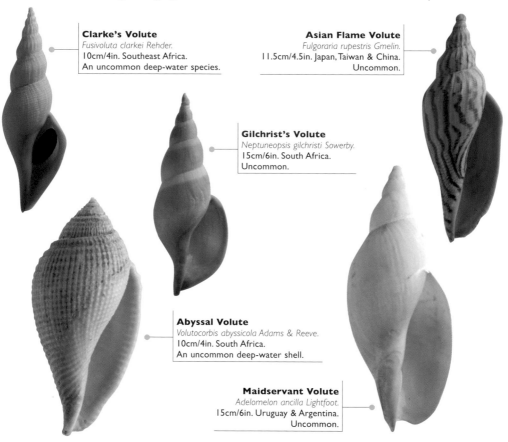

Clarke's Volute
Fusivoluta clarkei Rehder.
10cm/4in. Southeast Africa.
An uncommon deep-water species.

Asian Flame Volute
Fulgoraria rupestris Gmelin.
11.5cm/4.5in. Japan, Taiwan & China.
Uncommon.

Gilchrist's Volute
Neptuneopsis gilchristi Sowerby.
15cm/6in. South Africa.
Uncommon.

Abyssal Volute
Volutocorbis abyssicola Adams & Reeve.
10cm/4in. South Africa.
An uncommon deep-water shell.

Maidservant Volute
Adelomelon ancilla Lightfoot.
15cm/6in. Uruguay & Argentina.
Uncommon.

AUSTRALIAN VOLUTES

Many of the most attractive Volutes come from and are endemic to Australian seas. Many delicately patterned species such as Damon's and the Graceful Volute resemble fine porcelain.

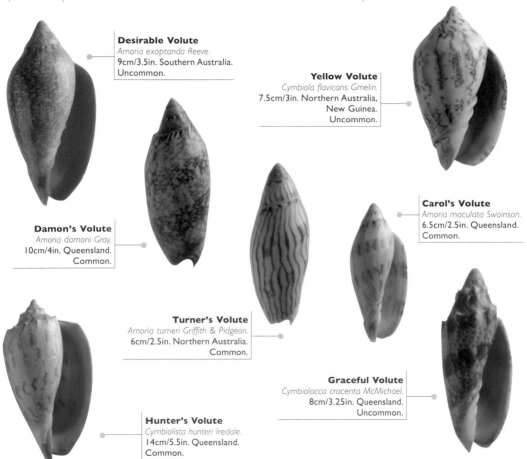

Desirable Volute
Amoria exoptanda Reeve.
9cm/3.5in. Southern Australia.
Uncommon.

Yellow Volute
Cymbiola flavicans Gmelin.
7.5cm/3in. Northern Australia,
New Guinea.
Uncommon.

Carol's Volute
Amoria maculata Swainson.
6.5cm/2.5in. Queensland.
Common.

Damon's Volute
Amoria damoni Gray.
10cm/4in. Queensland.
Common.

Turner's Volute
Amoria turneri Griffith & Pidgeon.
6cm/2.5in. Northern Australia.
Common.

Graceful Volute
Cymbiolacca cracenta McMichael.
8cm/3.25in. Queensland.
Uncommon.

Hunter's Volute
Cymbiolista hunteri Iredale.
14cm/5.5in. Queensland.
Common.

VOLUTE SHELLS

The famous Music Volute has a pattern that resembles old medieval chant music. There are several variations and forms. The Bat Volute, although uncommon, can be found in sinistral form in the Philippines. (See Shell Freaks and Abnormalities p232).

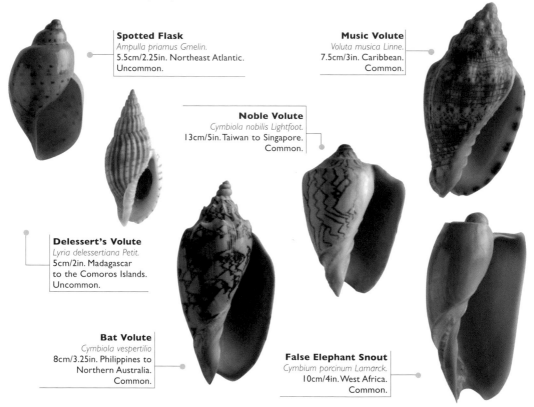

Spotted Flask
Ampulla priamus Gmelin.
5.5cm/2.25in. Northeast Atlantic.
Uncommon.

Music Volute
Voluta musica Linne.
7.5cm/3in. Caribbean.
Common.

Noble Volute
Cymbiola nobilis Lightfoot.
13cm/5in. Taiwan to Singapore.
Common.

Delessert's Volute
Lyria delessertiana Petit.
5cm/2in. Madagascar
to the Comoros Islands.
Uncommon.

Bat Volute
Cymbiola vespertilio
8cm/3.25in. Philippines to
Northern Australia.
Common.

False Elephant Snout
Cymbium porcinum Lamarck.
10cm/4in. West Africa.
Common.

UNCOMMON AND RARE VOLUTES

These are all collector's favourites and are keenly sought after. Most are expensive, some costing £100–200.

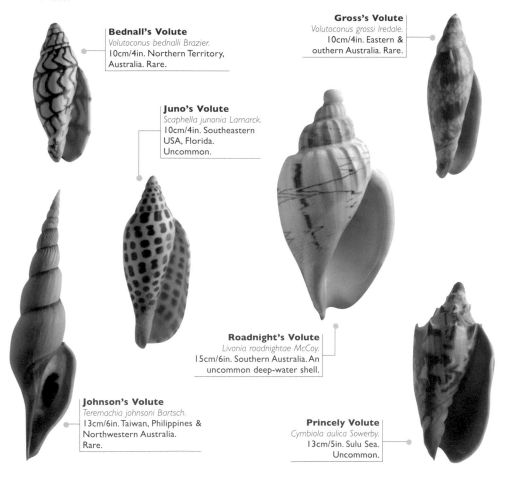

Bednall's Volute
Volutoconus bednalli Brazier.
10cm/4in. Northern Territory,
Australia. Rare.

Gross's Volute
Volutoconus grossi Iredale.
10cm/4in. Eastern &
outhern Australia. Rare.

Juno's Volute
Scaphella junonia Lamarck.
10cm/4in. Southeastern
USA, Florida.
Uncommon.

Roadnight's Volute
Livonia roadnightae McCoy.
15cm/6in. Southern Australia. An
uncommon deep-water shell.

Johnson's Volute
Teremachia johnsoni Bartsch.
13cm/6in. Taiwan, Philippines &
Northwestern Australia.
Rare.

Princely Volute
Cymbiola aulica Sowerby.
13cm/5in. Sulu Sea.
Uncommon.

HARP SHELLS

Harp Shells, Harpidae, are a small family comprising the genera Harpa, Austroharpa and Morum. The Harpa genus numbers about a dozen species.

They are all carnivorous and eat crustaceans. They inhabit mostly warm, shallow water on sandy substrates. A very popular collector's group. They are all attractive with strong ribs and colourful patterns.

Ventral Harp
Harpa ventricosa Lamarck.
8cm/3.25in. East & Southeast
Africa, Indian Ocean.
Common.

Major Harp
Harpa major Roding.
9cm/3.5in. Indo Pacific.
Common.

Minor Harp
Harpa amouretta Roding.
5cm/2in. Indo Pacific.
Common.

Articulate Harp
Harpa articularis Lamarck.
9cm/3.5in. Indo Pacific.
Common.

Rose Harp
Harpa doris Roding.
5.5cm/2.25in.
West Africa.
Uncommon.

Kajiyam's Harp
Harpa kajiyamai Rehder.
4.5cm/1.75in.
Western Pacific.
Rare.

True Harp
Harpa harpa Linne.
6cm/2.5in. Indo
Pacific. Common.

MORUM SHELLS

These shells were once considered as part of the Helmet (Cassidae) family, but are now included with the Harpidae. They are a small, interesting group of finely sculptured shells. Few, if any, are particularly common.

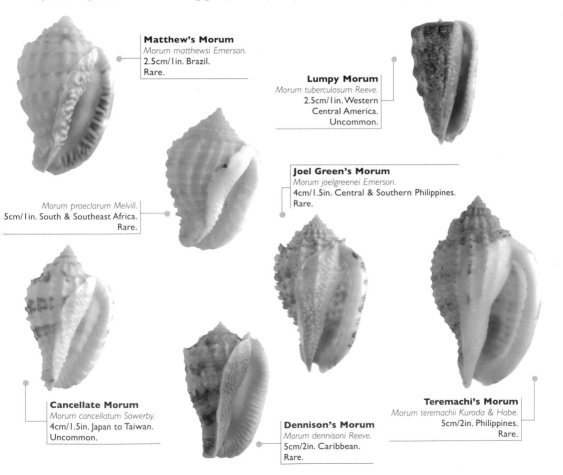

Matthew's Morum
Morum matthewsi Emerson.
2.5cm/1in. Brazil.
Rare.

Lumpy Morum
Morum tuberculosum Reeve.
2.5cm/1in. Western
Central America.
Uncommon.

Morum praeclarum Melvill.
5cm/1in. South & Southeast Africa.
Rare.

Joel Green's Morum
Morum joelgreenei Emerson.
4cm/1.5in. Central & Southern Philippines.
Rare.

Cancellate Morum
Morum cancellatum Sowerby.
4cm/1.5in. Japan to Taiwan.
Uncommon.

Dennison's Morum
Morum dennisoni Reeve.
5cm/2in. Caribbean.
Rare.

Teremachi's Morum
Morum teremachii Kuroda & Habe.
5cm/2in. Philippines.
Rare.

VASE SHELLS

Vase Shells (Vasidae) are coral-reef dwellers, with mostly medium to large, heavy, attractive shells. They are popular collector's shells.

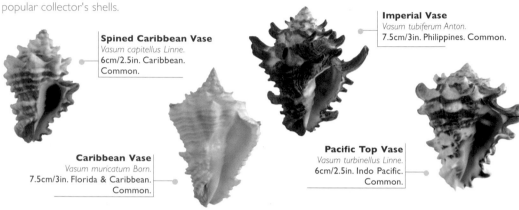

Spined Caribbean Vase
Vasum capitellus Linne.
6cm/2.5in. Caribbean.
Common.

Imperial Vase
Vasum tubiferum Anton.
7.5cm/3in. Philippines. Common.

Caribbean Vase
Vasum muricatum Born.
7.5cm/3in. Florida & Caribbean.
Common.

Pacific Top Vase
Vasum turbinellus Linne.
6cm/2.5in. Indo Pacific.
Common.

UNCOMMON AND RARE VASE SHELLS

Many of these species are rarely offered on dealers' lists and are collector's favourites.

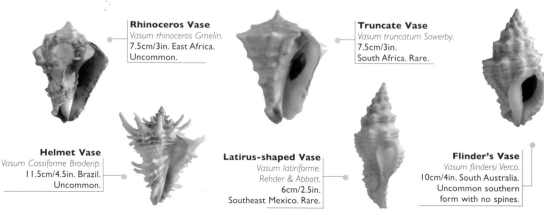

Rhinoceros Vase
Vasum rhinoceros Gmelin.
7.5cm/3in. East Africa.
Uncommon.

Truncate Vase
Vasum truncatum Sowerby.
7.5cm/3in.
South Africa. Rare.

Helmet Vase
Vasum Cassiforme Broderip.
11.5cm/4.5in. Brazil.
Uncommon.

Latirus-shaped Vase
Vasum latiriforme.
Rehder & Abbott.
6cm/2.5in.
Southeast Mexico. Rare.

Flinder's Vase
Vasum flindersi Verco.
10cm/4in. South Australia.
Uncommon southern
form with no spines.

CHANKS AND TUDICLAS

These shells are part of the Vasidae family. The Sacred Chank is a celebrated shell amongst Hindus and is used in religious ceremonies and for weddings, etc. Very rare sinistral specimens have in past times been gold-encrusted and are still much revered and sought after.

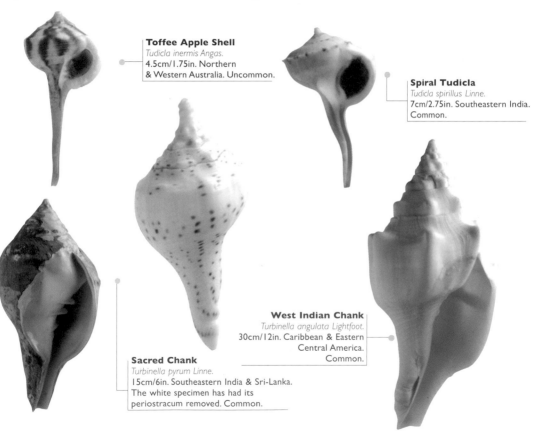

Toffee Apple Shell
Tudicla inermis Angas.
4.5cm/1.75in. Northern
& Western Australia. Uncommon.

Spiral Tudicla
Tudicla spirillus Linne.
7cm/2.75in. Southeastern India.
Common.

West Indian Chank
Turbinella angulata Lightfoot.
30cm/12in. Caribbean & Eastern
Central America.
Common.

Sacred Chank
Turbinella pyrum Linne.
15cm/6in. Southeastern India & Sri-Lanka.
The white specimen has had its
periostracum removed. Common.

PAGODA SHELLS

These very beautiful, delicate shells are also placed within the Vasidae family. Most species are deep-water shells and have no colouration or pattern.

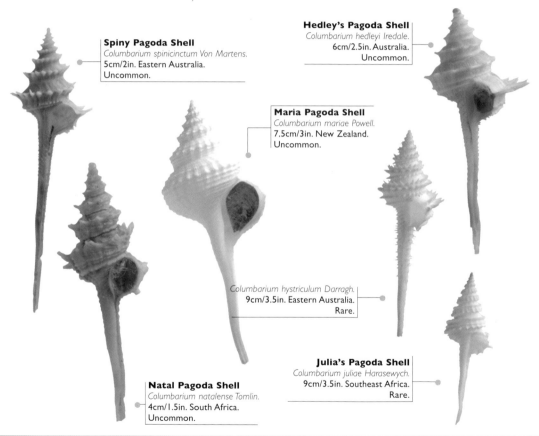

Hedley's Pagoda Shell
Columbarium hedleyi Iredale.
6cm/2.5in. Australia.
Uncommon.

Spiny Pagoda Shell
Columbarium spinicinctum Von Martens.
5cm/2in. Eastern Australia.
Uncommon.

Maria Pagoda Shell
Columbarium mariae Powell.
7.5cm/3in. New Zealand.
Uncommon.

Columbarium hystriculum Darragh.
9cm/3.5in. Eastern Australia.
Rare.

Julia's Pagoda Shell
Columbarium juliae Harasewych.
9cm/3.5in. Southeast Africa.
Rare.

Natal Pagoda Shell
Columbarium natalense Tomlin.
4cm/1.5in. South Africa.
Uncommon.

PAGODA SHELLS

Although Pagoda Shells are rare and inhabit deep water, some of these species occasionally appear in trawler-fishermen's nets in fine condition.

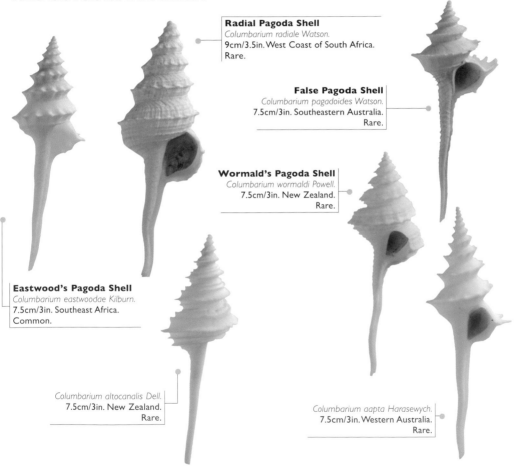

Radial Pagoda Shell
Columbarium radiale Watson.
9cm/3.5in. West Coast of South Africa.
Rare.

False Pagoda Shell
Columbarium pagadoides Watson.
7.5cm/3in. Southeastern Australia.
Rare.

Wormald's Pagoda Shell
Columbarium wormaldi Powell.
7.5cm/3in. New Zealand.
Rare.

Eastwood's Pagoda Shell
Columbarium eastwoodae Kilburn.
7.5cm/3in. Southeast Africa.
Common.

Columbarium altocanalis Dell.
7.5cm/3in. New Zealand.
Rare.

Columbarium aapta Harasewych.
7.5cm/3in. Western Australia.
Rare.

OLIVE SHELLS

The family Olividae is a large group of carnivorous Gastropods found in most warm tropical seas. They are night feeders.

Many species look similar and are often difficult to classify. The shells here are all from North and South America.

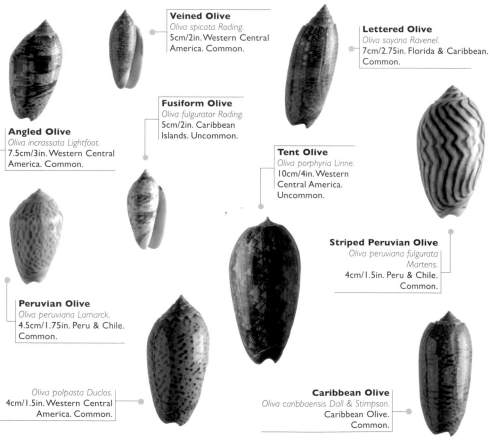

Veined Olive
Oliva spicata Roding.
5cm/2in. Western Central America. Common.

Lettered Olive
Oliva sayana Ravenel.
7cm/2.75in. Florida & Caribbean. Common.

Angled Olive
Oliva incrassata Lightfoot.
7.5cm/3in. Western Central America. Common.

Fusiform Olive
Oliva fulgurator Roding.
5cm/2in. Caribbean Islands. Uncommon.

Tent Olive
Oliva porphyria Linne.
10cm/4in. Western Central America. Uncommon.

Striped Peruvian Olive
Oliva peruviana fulgurata Martens.
4cm/1.5in. Peru & Chile. Common.

Peruvian Olive
Oliva peruviana Lamarck.
4.5cm/1.75in. Peru & Chile. Common.

Oliva polpasta Duclos.
4cm/1.5in. Western Central America. Common.

Caribbean Olive
Oliva caribbaensis Dall & Stimpson.
Caribbean Olive. Common.

OLIVE SHELLS

Olive Shell patterns and colours can vary considerably within the same species as the specimens shown here demonstrate. They are all very common shells.

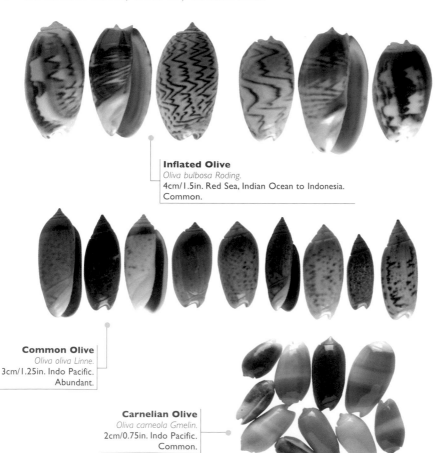

Inflated Olive
Oliva bulbosa Roding.
4cm/1.5in. Red Sea, Indian Ocean to Indonesia.
Common.

Common Olive
Oliva oliva Linne.
3cm/1.25in. Indo Pacific.
Abundant.

Carnelian Olive
Oliva carneola Gmelin.
2cm/0.75in. Indo Pacific.
Common.

WELL-KNOWN INDO-PACIFIC OLIVES

Blood Oliva
Oliva reticulata Roding.
5cm/2in.
Common.

Three-coloured Olive
Oliva tricolor Lamarck.
5cm/2in.
Common.

Tiger Olive
Oliva tigrina Lamarck.
5cm/2in.
Common.

Hirase's Olive
Oliva hirasei Kira.
5cm/2in.
Uncommon.

Gold-mouthed Olive
Oliva miniacea Roding.
10cm/4in.
Abundant.

Purple-mouthed Olive
Oliva caerulea Roding.
5cm/2in.
Common.

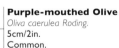

Textile Olive
Oliva textilina Lamarck.
9cm/3.5in.
Common.

PACIFIC OLIVE SHELLS

The Ornate Olive comes in varying forms, including an albino and deep orange form.

Blood-coloured Olive
Oliva annulata carnicolor Dautzenberg.
5cm/2in. Southwest Pacific.
Common.

Orange Ornate Olive
Oliva lignaria cryptospira Ford.
5cm/2in. Sulu Sea.
Common.

Old's Olive
Oliva tremulina oldi Zeigler.
5cm/2in. Southwest Pacific.
Uncommon.

Rounded Olive
Oliva bulbiformis Duclos.
4cm/1.5in. Indo Pacific.
Common.

Weasel Olive
Oliva mustellina Lamarck.
3cm/1.25in. Western Pacific.
Common.

Ornate Olive
Oliva lignaria Marrat.
5cm/2in. Indian Ocean & Western
Pacific. Common.

Reddish Olive
Oliva rufula Duclos.
3cm/1.25in. Southwest Pacific,
Philippines. Common.

UNCOMMON OLIVES

Some of these Olives inhabit quite restricted localities which renders them somewhat difficult to obtain.

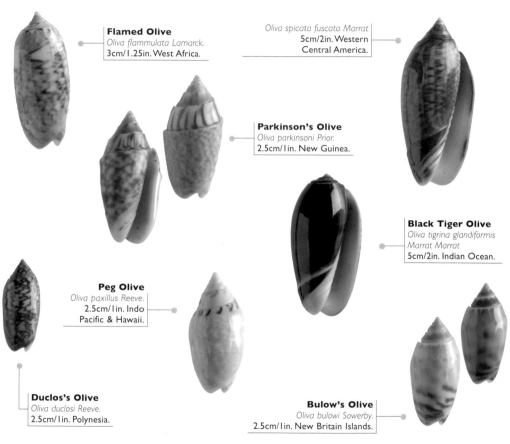

Flamed Olive
Oliva flammulata Lamarck.
3cm/1.25in. West Africa.

Oliva spicata fuscata Marrat
5cm/2in. Western
Central America.

Parkinson's Olive
Oliva parkinsoni Prior.
2.5cm/1in. New Guinea.

Black Tiger Olive
*Oliva tigrina glandiformis
Marrat Marrat*
5cm/2in. Indian Ocean.

Peg Olive
Oliva paxillus Reeve.
2.5cm/1in. Indo
Pacific & Hawaii.

Duclos's Olive
Oliva duclosi Reeve.
2.5cm/1in. Polynesia.

Bulow's Olive
Oliva bulowi Sowerby.
2.5cm/1in. New Britain Islands.

AMERICAN DWARF-OLIVES AND ANCILLAS

These shells are all in the Olividae. There are several main genera, including Olivancillaria, Olivella, Amalda and Agaronia.

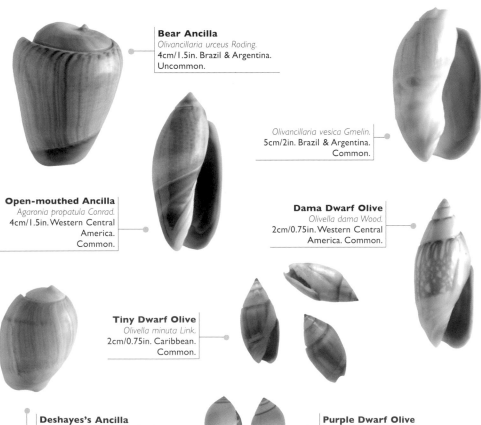

Bear Ancilla
Olivancillaria urceus Roding.
4cm/1.5in. Brazil & Argentina.
Uncommon.

Olivancillaria vesica Gmelin.
5cm/2in. Brazil & Argentina.
Common.

Open-mouthed Ancilla
Agaronia propatula Conrad.
4cm/1.5in. Western Central
America.
Common.

Dama Dwarf Olive
Olivella dama Wood.
2cm/0.75in. Western Central
America. Common.

Tiny Dwarf Olive
Olivella minuta Link.
2cm/0.75in. Caribbean.
Common.

Deshayes's Ancilla
Olivancillaria deshayesiana Duclos.
2.5cm/1in. Argentina.
Uncommon.

Purple Dwarf Olive
Olivella biplicata Sowerby.
2.5cm/1in. Vancouver to Baja California.
Common.

Gibbose Olive
Olivancillaria gibbosa Born.
5cm/2in. Southern India & Sri-Lanka.
Common.

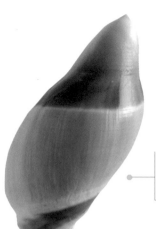

Urasima Ancilla
Baryspira urasima Kira.
4cm/1.5in. Japan.
Uncommon.

Mammal Ancilla
Amalda mamillata Hinds.
4cm/1.5in. Southwest Pacific.
Common.

Southern Ancilla
Amalda australis Sowerby.
3cm/1.25in. New Zealand.
Common.

Pointed Ancilla
Agaronia acuminata Lamarck.
6cm/2.5in. West Africa.
Common.

Margin Ancilla
Amalda marginarta Lamarck.
4cm/1.5in. Southern Australia.
Uncommon.

MARGIN SHELLS

The Marginellidae are a very large family comprising 600 named species of mainly small, smooth and colourful shells from worldwide habitats. The outer lip edges are usually thickened when adult, hence the name 'Margin' shell.

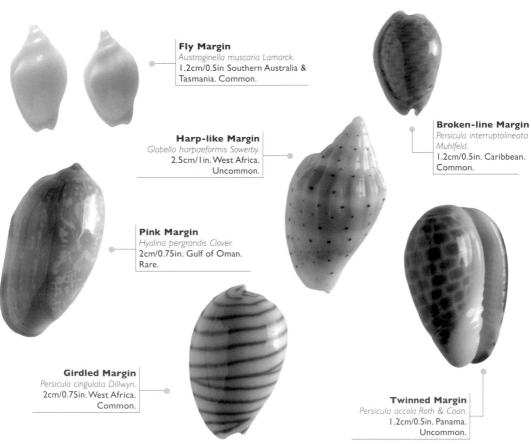

Fly Margin
Austroginella muscaria Lamarck.
1.2cm/0.5in Southern Australia & Tasmania. Common.

Broken-line Margin
Persicula interruptolineata Muhlfeld.
1.2cm/0.5in. Caribbean. Common.

Harp-like Margin
Glabella harpaeformis Sowerby.
2.5cm/1in. West Africa. Uncommon.

Pink Margin
Hyalina pergrandis Clover.
2cm/0.75in. Gulf of Oman. Rare.

Girdled Margin
Persicula cingulata Dillwyn.
2cm/0.75in. West Africa. Common.

Twinned Margin
Persicula accola Roth & Coan.
1.2cm/0.5in. Panama. Uncommon.

Golden Margin
Marginella aurantia Lamarck.
2.5cm/1in. West Africa.
Uncommon.

Adanson's Margin
Glabella adansoni Kiener.
2.5cm/1in. West Africa.
Uncommon.

Narrow Margin
Cryptospira angustata Sowerby.
2.5cm/1in. Southern India &
Sri Lanka. Common.

Clery's Margin
Marginella cleryii Petit.
2cm/0.75in. West Africa.
Uncommon.

Wonder Margin
Glabella mirabilis H. Adams.
2cm/0.75in. East Africa.
Rare.

Woolly Margin
Marginella floccata Sowerby.
2.5cm/1in. South Africa.
Uncommon.

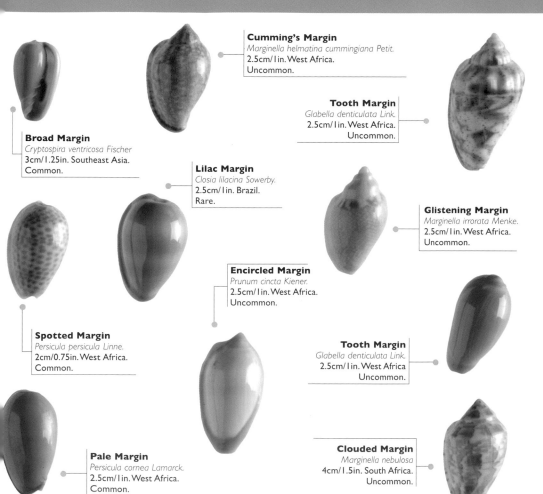

Cumming's Margin
Marginella helmatina cummingiana Petit.
2.5cm/1in. West Africa.
Uncommon.

Tooth Margin
Glabella denticulata Link.
2.5cm/1in. West Africa.
Uncommon.

Broad Margin
Cryptospira ventricosa Fischer
3cm/1.25in. Southeast Asia.
Common.

Lilac Margin
Closia lilacina Sowerby.
2.5cm/1in. Brazil.
Rare.

Glistening Margin
Marginella irrorata Menke.
2.5cm/1in. West Africa.
Uncommon.

Encircled Margin
Prunum cincta Kiener.
2.5cm/1in. West Africa.
Uncommon.

Spotted Margin
Persicula persicula Linne.
2cm/0.75in. West Africa.
Common.

Tooth Margin
Glabella denticulata Link.
2.5cm/1in. West Africa
Uncommon.

Pale Margin
Persicula cornea Lamarck.
2.5cm/1in. West Africa.
Common.

Clouded Margin
Marginella nebulosa
4cm/1.5in. South Africa.
Uncommon.

LARGER MARGIN SHELLS

Pringle's Margin was once considered to be a Volute Shell. It is the largest Margin species and inhabits deep water in South Africa.

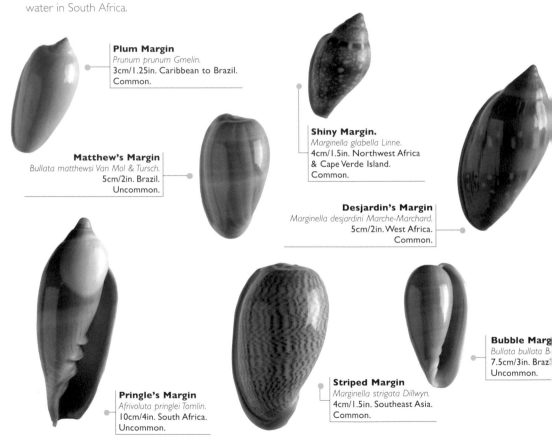

Plum Margin
Prunum prunum Gmelin.
3cm/1.25in. Caribbean to Brazil.
Common.

Matthew's Margin
Bullata matthewsi Van Mol & Tursch.
5cm/2in. Brazil.
Uncommon.

Shiny Margin.
Marginella glabella Linne.
4cm/1.5in. Northwest Africa
& Cape Verde Island.
Common.

Desjardin's Margin
Marginella desjardini Marche-Marchard.
5cm/2in. West Africa.
Common.

Pringle's Margin
Afrivoluta pringlei Tomlin.
10cm/4in. South Africa.
Uncommon.

Striped Margin
Marginella strigata Dillwyn.
4cm/1.5in. Southeast Asia.
Common.

Bubble Marg
Bullata bullata B
7.5cm/3in. Braz
Uncommon.

MITRE SHELLS

A large group of several hundred species, the Mitridae are split into numerous genera to account for both animal and shell variations. They are a popular family with collectors and enjoy worldwide distribution. The shells here are the larger members of the family.

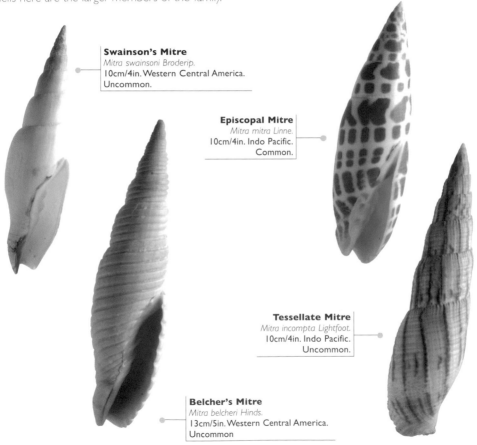

Swainson's Mitre
Mitra swainsoni Broderip.
10cm/4in. Western Central America.
Uncommon.

Episcopal Mitre
Mitra mitra Linne.
10cm/4in. Indo Pacific.
Common.

Tessellate Mitre
Mitra incompta Lightfoot.
10cm/4in. Indo Pacific.
Uncommon.

Belcher's Mitre
Mitra belcheri Hinds.
13cm/5in. Western Central America.
Uncommon

MITRE SHELLS

Most Mitres inhabit warm tropical seas and have colourful attractive shells.

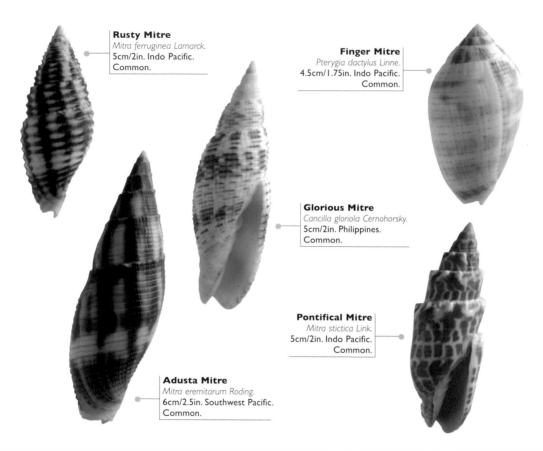

Rusty Mitre
Mitra ferruginea Lamarck.
5cm/2in. Indo Pacific.
Common.

Finger Mitre
Pterygia dactylus Linne.
4.5cm/1.75in. Indo Pacific.
Common.

Glorious Mitre
Cancilla gloriola Cernohorsky.
5cm/2in. Philippines.
Common.

Pontifical Mitre
Mitra stictica Link.
5cm/2in. Indo Pacific.
Common.

Adusta Mitre
Mitra eremitarum Roding.
6cm/2.5in. Southwest Pacific.
Common.

VEXILLUM MITRES

A beautiful genus of Mitres, these shells have tall, elegant spires with fine patterns and colours.

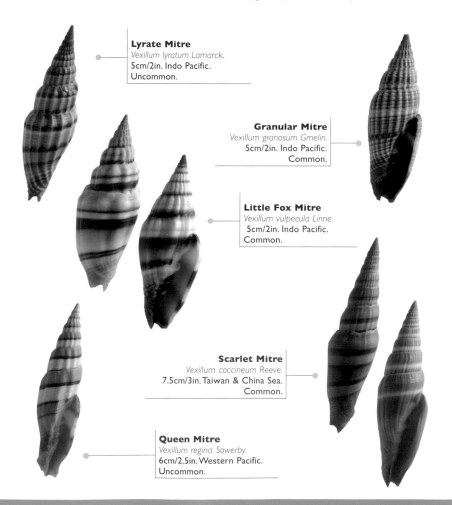

Lyrate Mitre
Vexillum lyratum Lamarck.
5cm/2in. Indo Pacific.
Uncommon.

Granular Mitre
Vexillum granosum Gmelin.
5cm/2in. Indo Pacific.
Common.

Little Fox Mitre
Vexillum vulpecula Linne.
5cm/2in. Indo Pacific.
Common.

Scarlet Mitre
Vexillum coccineum Reeve.
7.5cm/3in. Taiwan & China Sea.
Common.

Queen Mitre
Vexillum regina Sowerby.
6cm/2.5in. Western Pacific.
Uncommon.

SMALLER MITRES

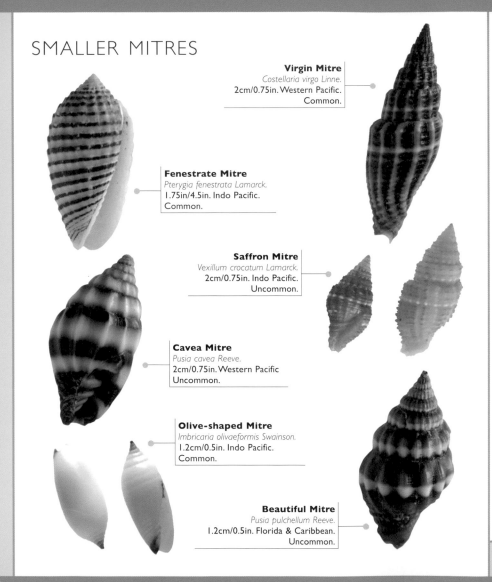

Virgin Mitre
Costellaria virgo Linne.
2cm/0.75in. Western Pacific.
Common.

Fenestrate Mitre
Pterygia fenestrata Lamarck.
1.75in/4.5in. Indo Pacific.
Common.

Saffron Mitre
Vexillum crocatum Lamarck.
2cm/0.75in. Indo Pacific.
Uncommon.

Cavea Mitre
Pusia cavea Reeve.
2cm/0.75in. Western Pacific
Uncommon.

Olive-shaped Mitre
Imbricaria olivaeformis Swainson.
1.2cm/0.5in. Indo Pacific.
Common.

Beautiful Mitre
Pusia pulchellum Reeve.
1.2cm/0.5in. Florida & Caribbean.
Uncommon.

Hansen's Mitre
Pusia hansenae Cernohorsky.
1.2cm/0.5in. Western Australia.
Uncommon.

Pusia amabilis Reeve.
2cm/0.75in. Indo Pacific.
Uncommon.

Costellaria leucozonias Deshayes.
1.2cm/0.5in.
Central & Western Pacific.
Uncommon..

Strigatella peculiaris Reeve.
1.2cm/0.5in. Western Pacific.
Uncommon.

Ringed Mitre
Subcancilla annulata Reeve.
2cm/0.75in. Indo Pacific.
Common.

Costellaria zelotypum Reeve.
2.5cm/1in. Western Pacific.
Common.

MITRE SHELLS

Acuminate Mitre
Mitra acuminata Swainson.
5cm/2in. Indian Ocean.
Uncommon.

Rugose Mitre
Vexillum rugosum Gmelin.
5cm/2in. Indo Pacific.
Common.

Gruner's Mitre
Vexillum gruneri Reeve.
2.5cm/1in. Indo Pacific.
Common.

Bloodsucker Mitre
Vexillum sanguisugum Linne.
5cm/2in. Indo Pacific.
Uncommon.

Roughened Mitre
Vexillum exasperatum Gmelin.
2.5cm/1in. Indo Pacific.
Common.

Ziervogeli's Mitre
Zierliana zeirvogelii Gmelin.
2.5cm/1in. Philippines.
Uncommon.

UNCOMMON AND RARE MITRES

Stainforth's Mitre
Vexillum stainforthi Reeve.
4cm/1.5in. Southwest Pacific.
Uncommon.

Bove's Mitre
Mitra bovei Kiener
5cm/2in. Red Sea & Northeast
Indian Ocean. Rare.

Victor Dan's Mitre
Scabricola vicdani Cernohorsky.
5cm/2in. Philippines.
Uncommon.

Ziba fulgetrum Reeve.
2cm/0.75in. Western Pacific.
Uncommon.

Florida Mitre
Dibaphus florida Gould.
5cm/2in. Florida & Caribbean.
Rare.

Newcomb's Mitra
Scabricola newcombii Pease.
2.5cm/1in. Hawaii & Midway Islands.
Rare.

Reticulate Mitre
*Scabricola fissurata
Lamarck.*
5cm/2in. East Africa & Red
Sea. Uncommon.

Helen's Mitre
Mitra helenae Radwin & Bibbey.
6cm/2.5in. Honduras &
Nicaragua.
Rare.

Dennison's Mitre
Vexillum dennisoni Reeve.
6cm/2.5in. Philippines.
Uncommon.

NUTMEGS

A group of snails with fascinating sculpturing and shape, the Cancellariidae enjoy living in warm seas in moderate to deep water. Little is known of their feeding habits, but they possibly eat shell-less micro organisms on the sea bed.

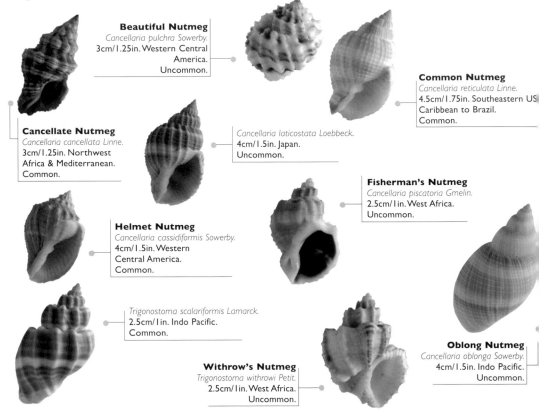

Beautiful Nutmeg
Cancellaria pulchra Sowerby.
3cm/1.25in. Western Central America.
Uncommon.

Common Nutmeg
Cancellaria reticulata Linne.
4.5cm/1.75in. Southeastern US Caribbean to Brazil.
Common.

Cancellate Nutmeg
Cancellaria cancellata Linne.
3cm/1.25in. Northwest Africa & Mediterranean.
Common.

Cancellaria laticostata Loebbeck.
4cm/1.5in. Japan.
Uncommon.

Fisherman's Nutmeg
Cancellaria piscatoria Gmelin.
2.5cm/1in. West Africa.
Uncommon.

Helmet Nutmeg
Cancellaria cassidiformis Sowerby.
4cm/1.5in. Western Central America.
Common.

Trigonostoma scalariformis Lamarck.
2.5cm/1in. Indo Pacific.
Common.

Withrow's Nutmeg
Trigonostoma withrowi Petit.
2.5cm/1in. West Africa.
Uncommon.

Oblong Nutmeg
Cancellaria oblonga Sowerby.
4cm/1.5in. Indo Pacific.
Uncommon.

Rounded Nutmeg
Cancellaria bulbulus Sowerby.
4.5cm/1.75in. Western
Central America.
Common.

Petuch's Nutmeg
Cancellaria petuchi Harasewych,
Petit & Verharghe.
3cm/1.25in. Brazil.
Uncommon.

Knobbed Nutmeg
Cancellaria nodulifera
Sowerby.
4.5cm/1.75in. Japan.
Uncommon.

Toothed Nutmeg
Cancellaria indentata Sowerby.
2.5cm/1in. Western Central
America. Common.

Western Australian Nutmeg
Cancellaria westralis Garrard.
2.5cm/1in. Western Australia.
Uncommon.

Crenulated Nutmeg
Trigonostoma crenifera Sowerby.
2.5cm/1in. Indo Pacific.
Common.

Dim Nutmeg
Cancellaria urceolata Hinds.
2.5cm/1in. Western Central
America. Common.

Rigid Nutmeg
Cancellaria rigida Sowerby.
2cm/0.75in. West Africa.
Uncommon.

Hollow Nutmeg
Scalptia foveolata Sowerby.
2cm/0.75in. South Africa.
Uncommon.

RARER NUTMEGS

Miller's Nutmeg is a unique species with open whorls. Both Miller's Nutmeg and the Little Elegant Nutmeg are much sought after by collectors.

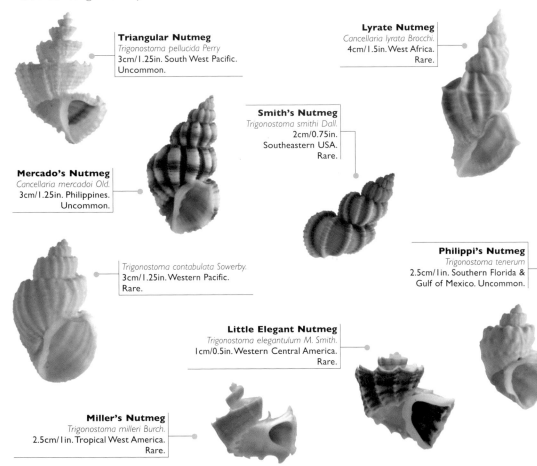

Triangular Nutmeg
Trigonostoma pellucida Perry
3cm/1.25in. South West Pacific.
Uncommon.

Lyrate Nutmeg
Cancellaria lyrata Brocchi.
4cm/1.5in. West Africa.
Rare.

Smith's Nutmeg
Trigonostoma smithi Dall.
2cm/0.75in.
Southeastern USA.
Rare.

Mercado's Nutmeg
Cancellaria mercadoi Old.
3cm/1.25in. Philippines.
Uncommon.

Trigonostoma contabulata Sowerby.
3cm/1.25in. Western Pacific.
Rare.

Philippi's Nutmeg
Trigonostoma tenerum
2.5cm/1in. Southern Florida &
Gulf of Mexico. Uncommon.

Little Elegant Nutmeg
Trigonostoma elegantulum M. Smith.
1cm/0.5in. Western Central America.
Rare.

Miller's Nutmeg
Trigonostoma milleri Burch.
2.5cm/1in. Tropical West America.
Rare.

CONE SHELLS

A large family, the Conidae number over 300 species and are possibly the most popular collector group after the Cowries. They are a very successful predacious family feeding on worms, molluscs and fish. They have a highly developed radula system by which they are able to inject poisonous barbs into their prey prior to feeding. All Cones are covered by a thick periostracum when alive. The shells depicted here are all well-known and common Indo-Pacific species.

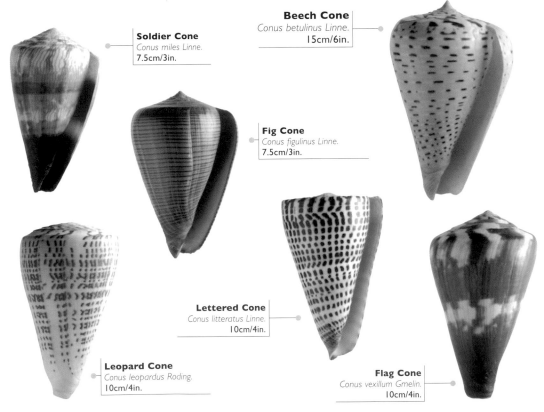

Soldier Cone
Conus miles Linne.
7.5cm/3in.

Beech Cone
Conus betulinus Linne.
15cm/6in.

Fig Cone
Conus figulinus Linne.
7.5cm/3in.

Lettered Cone
Conus litteratus Linne.
10cm/4in.

Leopard Cone
Conus leopardus Roding.
10cm/4in.

Flag Cone
Conus vexillum Gmelin.
10cm/4in.

COMMON INDO-PACIFIC CONES

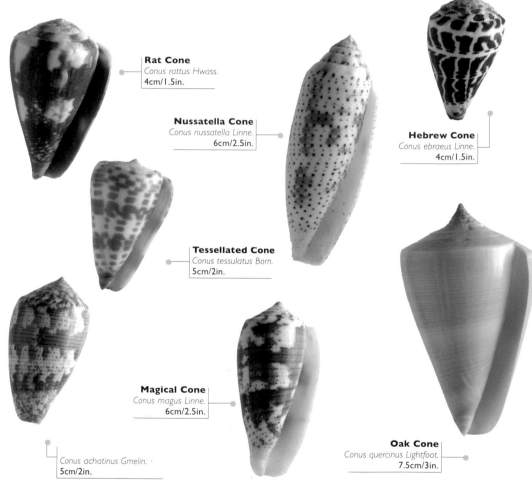

Rat Cone
Conus rattus Hwass.
4cm/1.5in.

Nussatella Cone
Conus nussatella Linne.
6cm/2.5in.

Hebrew Cone
Conus ebraeus Linne.
4cm/1.5in.

Tessellated Cone
Conus tessulatus Born.
5cm/2in.

Magical Cone
Conus magus Linne.
6cm/2.5in.

Conus achatinus Gmelin.
5cm/2in.

Oak Cone
Conus quercinus Lightfoot.
7.5cm/3in.

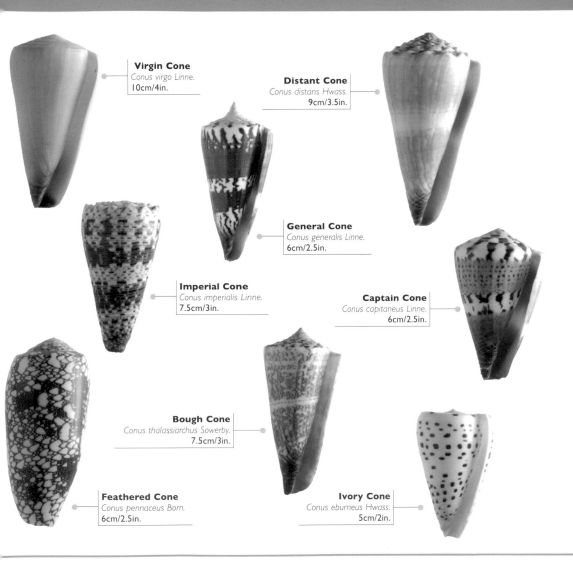

Virgin Cone
Conus virgo Linne.
10cm/4in.

Distant Cone
Conus distans Hwass.
9cm/3.5in.

General Cone
Conus generalis Linne.
6cm/2.5in.

Imperial Cone
Conus imperialis Linne.
7.5cm/3in.

Captain Cone
Conus capitaneus Linne.
6cm/2.5in.

Bough Cone
Conus thalassiarchus Sowerby.
7.5cm/3in.

Feathered Cone
Conus pennaceus Born.
6cm/2.5in.

Ivory Cone
Conus eburneus Hwass.
5cm/2in.

COMMON FROM WESTERN CENTRAL AND SOUTH AMERICA

Ferguson's Cone
Conus fergusoni Sowerby.
9cm/3.5in. Tropical West America.
Common.

Purple Cone
Conus purpurascens Sowerby.
6cm/2.5in. Western Central America.
Common.

Clery's Cone
Conus clerii Reeve.
4cm/1.5in. Brazil
& Northern Argentina.
Uncommon.

Virgate Panama Cone
Conus virgatus Reeve.
5cm/2in. Western Central America.
Uncommon.

Magistrate Cone
Conus archon Broderip.
5cm/2in. Western
Central America.
Uncommon.

Regular Cone
Conus regularis Sowerby.
4cm/1.5in. Western
Central America.
Common.

Interrupted Cone
Conus ximenes Gray.
4.5cm/1.75in. Western
Central America. Common.

Ribboned Cone
Conus vittatus Hwass.
3cm/1.25in. Western Central America.
Rare.

Arched Cone
Conus arcuatus Broderip & Sowerby.
4.5cm/1.75in. Western
Central America.
Uncommon.

CARIBBEAN CONES

The Bermuda and Centurio Cones are difficult-to-obtain, collector's items.

Conus mindanus Hwass.
2.5cm/1in.
Uncommon.

Florida Cone
Conus floridanus Gabb.
4cm/1.5in. Southeast USA.
Common.

Bermuda Cone
Conus bermudiensis Clench.
2.5cm/1in. West Indies.
Rare.

Centurion Cone
Conus centurio Born.
5cm/2in.
Uncommon.

Alphabet Cone
Conus spurius Gmelin.
5cm/2in. Southeast USA & West Indies.
Common.

Turtle Cone
Conus ermineus Born.
5cm/2in. West Indies (& West Africa).
Common.

CONES FROM WEST AFRICA AND CAPE VERDE ISLANDS

The Cones from the Cape Verde Islands are a totally unique group, occurring nowhere else in the world and comprise possibly twenty or more species of mostly small Cones.

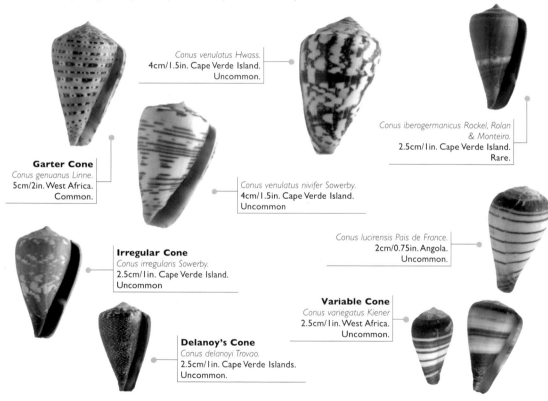

Conus venulatus Hwass.
4cm/1.5in. Cape Verde Island.
Uncommon.

Conus iberogermanicus Rockel, Rolan & Monteiro.
2.5cm/1in. Cape Verde Island.
Rare.

Garter Cone
Conus genuanus Linne.
5cm/2in. West Africa.
Common.

Conus venulatus nivifer Sowerby.
4cm/1.5in. Cape Verde Island.
Uncommon

Conus lucirensis Pais de France.
2cm/0.75in. Angola.
Uncommon.

Irregular Cone
Conus irregularis Sowerby.
2.5cm/1in. Cape Verde Island.
Uncommon

Variable Cone
Conus variegatus Kiener
2.5cm/1in. West Africa.
Uncommon.

Delanoy's Cone
Conus delanoyi Trovao.
2.5cm/1in. Cape Verde Islands.
Uncommon.

168

UNCOMMON CONES

Beddome's Cone
Conus beddomei Sowerby.
2.5cm/1in. Brazil.

Don Bosch's Cone
Conus boschi Melvill.
2.5cm/1in. Gulf of Oman.

Cabrit's Cone
Conus cabritti Bernardi.
2.5cm/1in. Western Pacific.

Obscure Cone
Conus obscurus Sowerby.
2.5cm/1in. Western Pacific.

Mitre-shaped Cone
Conus mitratus Hwass.
2.5cm/1in. Western Pacific.

Spindle Cone
Conus aculeiformis Reeve.
3.5cm/1.5in. Indo Pacific.

Conus proximus Sowerby.
3.5cm/1.5in. Western Pacific.

Violet Cone
Conus viola Cernohorsky.
3cm/1.25in. Western Pacific.

UNCOMMON CONES

The Striated Cone is very common, but this form from Reunion Islands is a rare colour variation. The Bubble Cone, although uncommon, can be collected in great numbers on beaches after tropical storms in the Solomon Islands.

Vautier's Cone
Conus pulicarius vautieri Kiener.
4cm/1.75in.
Marquesas Islands.

Conus textile euetrios Sowerby.
5.5cm/2.25in. East &
Southeast Africa.

Thunderbolt Cone
Conus fulmen Reeve.
5cm/2in. Japan

Smoky Cone
Conus fumigatus Hwass.
3.5cm/1.5in. Red Sea, Ethiopia.

Hyena Cone
Conus hyaena Hwass.
5cm/2in.
Southern India.

Kinoshita's Cone
Conus kinoshitai Kuroda.
7cm/2.75in.
Western Pacific.

Ichinose Cone
Conus ichinoseana Kuroda.
6cm/2.5in. Japan to the Philippines.

Striated Cone
Conus striatus Linne.
10cm/4in. Reunion Islands form.

Bubble Cone
Conus bullatus Linne.
6cm/2.5in. Indo Pacific.

HIGHLY TOXIC CONES

These mostly fish-eating species – usually identified by wide, flaring mouths – are capable of inflicting serious toxic stings. The Geography Cone, amongst others, is know to have claimed human fatalities due to careless handling when collecting live shells.

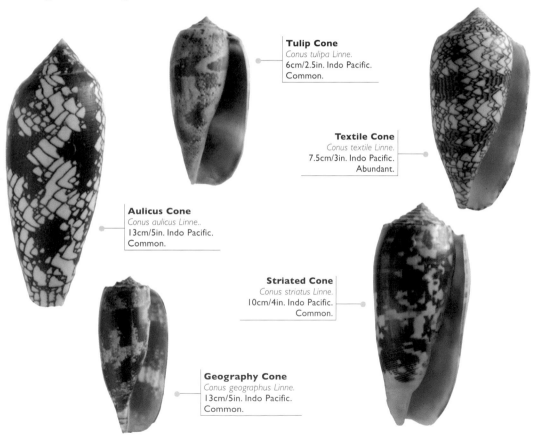

Tulip Cone
Conus tulipa Linne.
6cm/2.5in. Indo Pacific.
Common.

Textile Cone
Conus textile Linne.
7.5cm/3in. Indo Pacific.
Abundant.

Aulicus Cone
Conus aulicus Linne..
13cm/5in. Indo Pacific.
Common.

Striated Cone
Conus striatus Linne.
10cm/4in. Indo Pacific.
Common.

Geography Cone
Conus geographus Linne.
13cm/5in. Indo Pacific.
Common.

the glory of the sea cone

The most sought-after of all seashells, every collector wants to own Conus gloriamaris Chemnitz. Its very name suggests a rare treasure from the deep. For centuries, the most valuable and coveted species, only very few ever changed hands at auctions at incredible prices.

Little was known of its habitat until two were found by Hugh Cumming in 1836 in the Philippines. Very few since then came to light until the late 1960s. It was still considered an ultra-rare shell at that time as only a few dozen were held in private or museum collections. Nowadays, the habitat is well known – moderately deep water in the Central Philippines. The shells can reach 15cm/6in. but these are scarce; they usually attain 10-13cm/4–5in. Fine- to gem-quality specimens can still cost between £100–200, but, comparatively, this is far less expensive than shells sold or auctioned in the 18th and 19th centuries.

It is perhaps not the most beautiful of Cones, but it is elegant, with fine tent markings. Possibly the sole reason for its fame is its name.

RARE CONES

Most of these Cones are more scarce than Conus gloriamaris – in particular the Illustrious and Palissade Cones. Dealers only offer these occasionally, and at high prices.

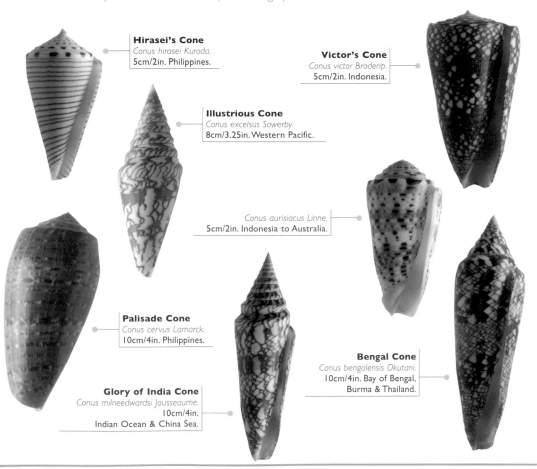

Hirasei's Cone
Conus hirasei Kuroda.
5cm/2in. Philippines.

Victor's Cone
Conus victor Broderip.
5cm/2in. Indonesia.

Illustrious Cone
Conus excelsus Sowerby.
8cm/3.25in. Western Pacific.

Conus aurisiacus Linne.
5cm/2in. Indonesia to Australia.

Palisade Cone
Conus cervus Lamarck.
10cm/4in. Philippines.

Bengal Cone
Conus bengalensis Okutani.
10cm/4in. Bay of Bengal,
Burma & Thailand.

Glory of India Cone
Conus milneedwardsi Jousseaume.
10cm/4in.
Indian Ocean & China Sea.

CONES IN THE MARMOREUS GROUP

Marble Cones all have distinctive marbling and are all popular with collectors.

Banded Marble Cone
Conus marmoreus bandanus Hwass.
Indian Ocean.
Common.

Nicobar Cone
Conus nicobaricus Hwass.
6.5cm/2.5in. India to the Philippines.
Common.

Vidua Cone
Conus vidua Reeve.
7.5cm/3in. Indo Pacific.
Common.

Marble Cone
Conus marmoreus Linne.
10cm/4in. Indo Pacific.
Common.

Marble Cone
Conus marmoreus Linne.
6cm/2.5in. New Caledonian
variation.
Uncommon.

Marble Cone
Conus marmoreus Linne.
7.5cm/3in. Pattern variation
Philippines.
Uncommon.

AUSTRALIAN AND SOUTH AFRICAN CONES

Until the late 1970s, most South African Cones were only known from worn, beached specimens until the growth in popularity of scuba diving.

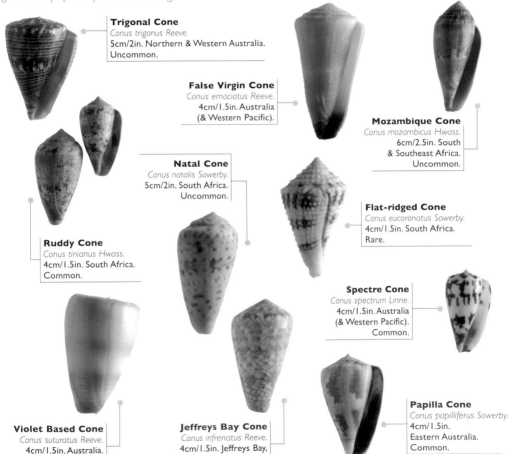

Trigonal Cone
Conus trigonus Reeve.
5cm/2in. Northern & Western Australia.
Uncommon.

False Virgin Cone
Conus emaciatus Reeve.
4cm/1.5in. Australia
(& Western Pacific).

Mozambique Cone
Conus mozambicus Hwass.
6cm/2.5in. South
& Southeast Africa.
Uncommon.

Natal Cone
Conus natalis Sowerby.
5cm/2in. South Africa.
Uncommon.

Flat-ridged Cone
Conus eucoronatus Sowerby.
4cm/1.5in. South Africa.
Rare.

Ruddy Cone
Conus tinianus Hwass.
4cm/1.5in. South Africa.
Common.

Spectre Cone
Conus spectrum Linne.
4cm/1.5in. Australia
(& Western Pacific).
Common.

Violet Based Cone
Conus suturatus Reeve.
4cm/1.5in. Australia.
Common.

Jeffreys Bay Cone
Conus infrenatus Reeve.
4cm/1.5in. Jeffreys Bay,
South Africa. Common.

Papilla Cone
Conus papilliferus Sowerby.
4cm/1.5in.
Eastern Australia.
Common.

TURRID SHELLS

The family Turridae is the largest group of shells, numbering in excess of 1,000 species. Most are fairly small shells; all have pronounced spires and a characteristic slit-like anal notch on the upper edge of the lip. They are carnivorous and inhabit worldwide localities in both shallow and very deep water. The shells shown here are all well-known species.

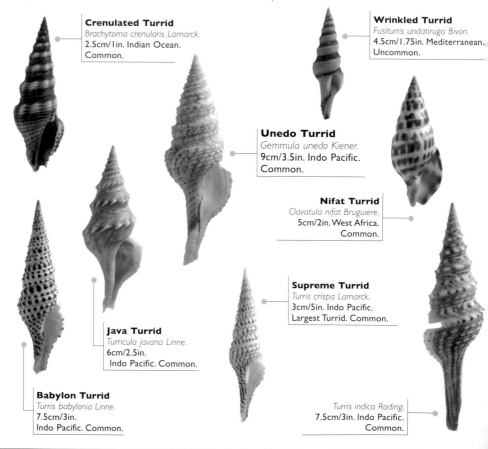

Crenulated Turrid
Brachytoma crenularis Lamarck.
2.5cm/1in. Indian Ocean.
Common.

Wrinkled Turrid
Fusiturris undatiruga Bivon.
4.5cm/1.75in. Mediterranean.
Uncommon.

Unedo Turrid
Gemmula unedo Kiener.
9cm/3.5in. Indo Pacific.
Common.

Nifat Turrid
Clavatula nifat Bruguiere.
5cm/2in. West Africa.
Common.

Supreme Turrid
Turris crispa Lamarck.
3cm/5in. Indo Pacific.
Largest Turrid. Common.

Java Turrid
Turricula javana Linne.
6cm/2.5in.
Indo Pacific. Common.

Babylon Turrid
Turris babylonia Linne.
7.5cm/3in.
Indo Pacific. Common.

Turris indica Roding.
7.5cm/3in. Indo Pacific.
Common.

JAPANESE AND PHILIPPINO TURRIDS

Both Graeffe's and the Dull Star Turrid are sought-after collector's items.

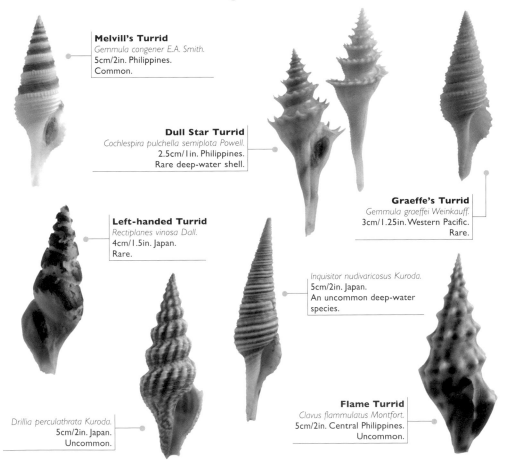

Melvill's Turrid
Gemmula congener E.A. Smith.
5cm/2in. Philippines.
Common.

Dull Star Turrid
Cochlespira pulchella semiplota Powell.
2.5cm/1in. Philippines.
Rare deep-water shell.

Graeffe's Turrid
Gemmula graeffei Weinkauff.
3cm/1.25in. Western Pacific.
Rare.

Left-handed Turrid
Rectiplanes vinosa Dall.
4cm/1.5in. Japan.
Rare.

Inquisitor nudivaricosus Kuroda.
5cm/2in. Japan.
An uncommon deep-water
species.

Drillia perculathrata Kuroda.
5cm/2in. Japan.
Uncommon.

Flame Turrid
Clavus flammulatus Montfort.
5cm/2in. Central Philippines.
Uncommon.

TURRIDS FROM CENTRAL AND SOUTH AMERICA

Some of these shells, such as the Chilean Turrid and Crassispira amathea, are rare in amateur collections .

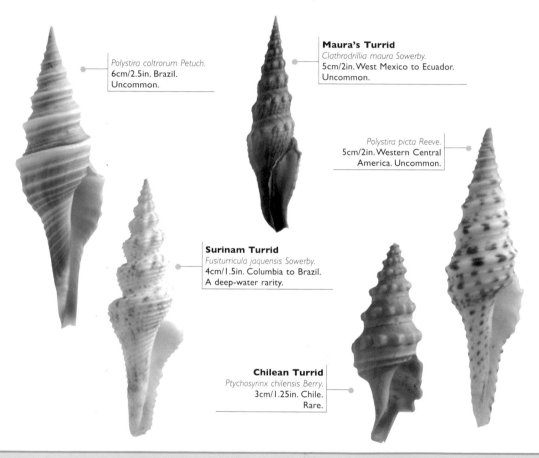

Polystira coltrorum Petuch.
6cm/2.5in. Brazil.
Uncommon.

Maura's Turrid
Clathrodrillia maura Sowerby.
5cm/2in. West Mexico to Ecuador.
Uncommon.

Polystira picta Reeve.
5cm/2in. Western Central
America. Uncommon.

Surinam Turrid
Fusiturricula jaquensis Sowerby.
4cm/1.5in. Columbia to Brazil.
A deep-water rarity.

Chilean Turrid
Ptychosyrinx chilensis Berry.
3cm/1.25in. Chile.
Rare.

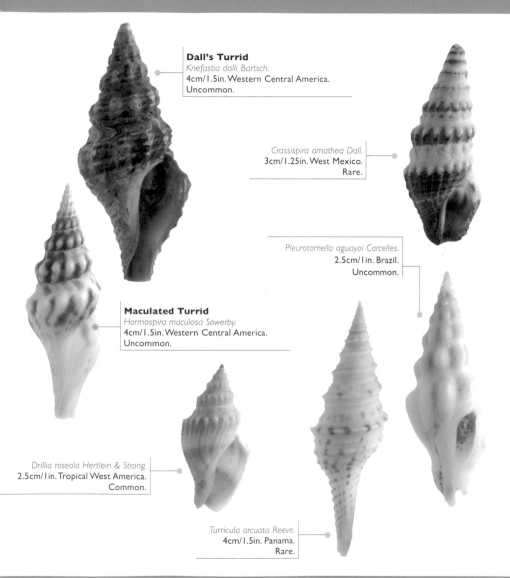

Dall's Turrid
Knefastia dalli Bartsch.
4cm/1.5in. Western Central America.
Uncommon.

Crassispira amathea Dall.
3cm/1.25in. West Mexico.
Rare.

Pleurotomella aguayoi Carcelles.
2.5cm/1in. Brazil.
Uncommon.

Maculated Turrid
Hormospira maculosa Sowerby.
4cm/1.5in. Western Central America.
Uncommon.

Drillia roseola Hertlein & Strong.
2.5cm/1in. Tropical West America.
Common.

Turricula arcuata Reeve.
4cm/1.5in. Panama.
Rare.

AUSTRALIAN TURRIDS

Several of these species are only occasionally fished in very deep water off Northwestern Australia.

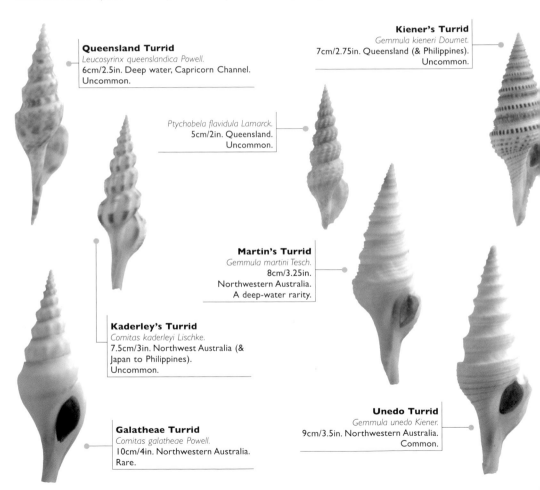

Queensland Turrid
Leucosyrinx queenslandica Powell.
6cm/2.5in. Deep water, Capricorn Channel.
Uncommon.

Kiener's Turrid
Gemmula kieneri Doumet.
7cm/2.75in. Queensland (& Philippines).
Uncommon.

Ptychobela flavidula Lamarck.
5cm/2in. Queensland.
Uncommon.

Martin's Turrid
Gemmula martini Tesch.
8cm/3.25in.
Northwestern Australia.
A deep-water rarity.

Kaderley's Turrid
Comitas kaderleyi Lischke.
7.5cm/3in. Northwest Australia (&
Japan to Philippines).
Uncommon.

Galatheae Turrid
Comitas galatheae Powell.
10cm/4in. Northwestern Australia.
Rare.

Unedo Turrid
Gemmula unedo Kiener.
9cm/3.5in. Northwestern Australia.
Common.

SOUTH AFRICAN TURRIDS

Most of these deep, cooler water Turrids have little or no colouration.

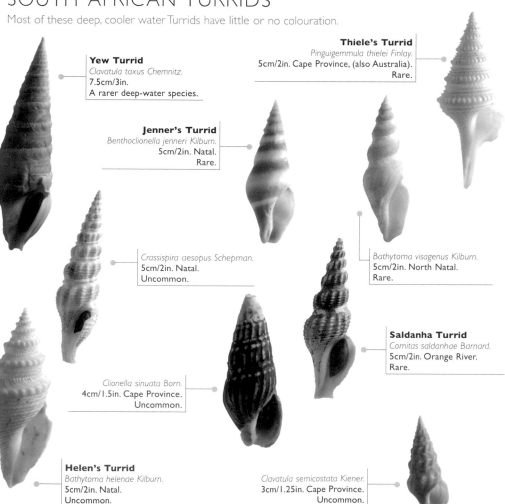

Yew Turrid
Clavatula taxus Chemnitz.
7.5cm/3in.
A rarer deep-water species.

Thiele's Turrid
Pinguigemmula thielei Finlay.
5cm/2in. Cape Province, (also Australia).
Rare.

Jenner's Turrid
Benthoclionella jenneri Kilburn.
5cm/2in. Natal.
Rare.

Crassispira aesopus Schepman.
5cm/2in. Natal.
Uncommon.

Bathytoma visagenus Kilburn.
5cm/2in. North Natal.
Rare.

Saldanha Turrid
Comitas saldanhae Barnard.
5cm/2in. Orange River.
Rare.

Clionella sinuata Born.
4cm/1.5in. Cape Province.
Uncommon.

Helen's Turrid
Bathytoma helenae Kilburn.
5cm/2in. Natal.
Uncommon.

Clavatula semicostata Kiener.
3cm/1.25in. Cape Province.
Uncommon.

auger shells

The Augers (Terebridae) are carnivorous inhabitants of warm seas. They live in sand and possess a thin horny operculum. Unlike many highly glossy shells, they are not covered with a periostracum when alive. They all have characteristic tall, slender spires.

There are perhaps 300 species. Most shells here are common, well-known species.

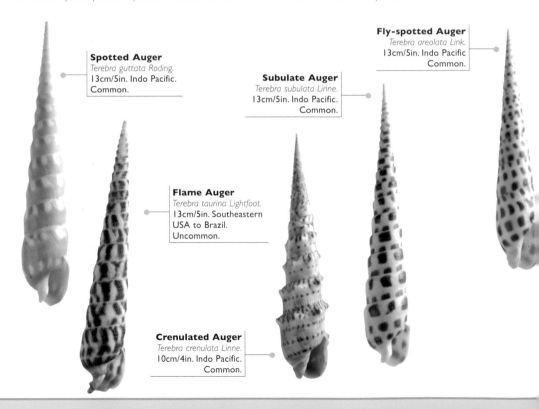

Fly-spotted Auger
Terebra areolata Link.
13cm/5in. Indo Pacific.
Common.

Spotted Auger
Terebra guttata Roding.
13cm/5in. Indo Pacific.
Common.

Subulate Auger
Terebra subulata Linne.
13cm/5in. Indo Pacific.
Common.

Flame Auger
Terebra taurina Lightfoot.
13cm/5in. Southeastern
USA to Brazil.
Uncommon.

Crenulated Auger
Terebra crenulata Linne.
10cm/4in. Indo Pacific.
Common.

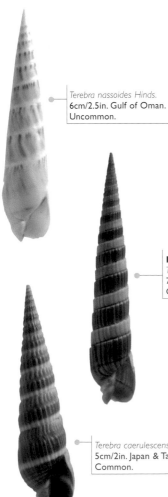

Faval Auger
Terebra senegalensis Lamarck.
6cm/2.5in. West Africa.
Uncommon.

Terebra nassoides Hinds.
6cm/2.5in. Gulf of Oman.
Uncommon.

Ornate Auger
Terebra ornata Gray.
9cm/3.5in. Western Central America
& Galapagos Islands.
Uncommon.

Duplicate Auger
Terebra duplicata
7.5cm/3in. Indo Pacific.
Common.

Short Auger
Terebra chlorata Lamarck.
6cm/2.5in. Indo Pacific.
Common.

Terebra caerulescens Lamarck.
5cm/2in. Japan & Taiwan.
Common.

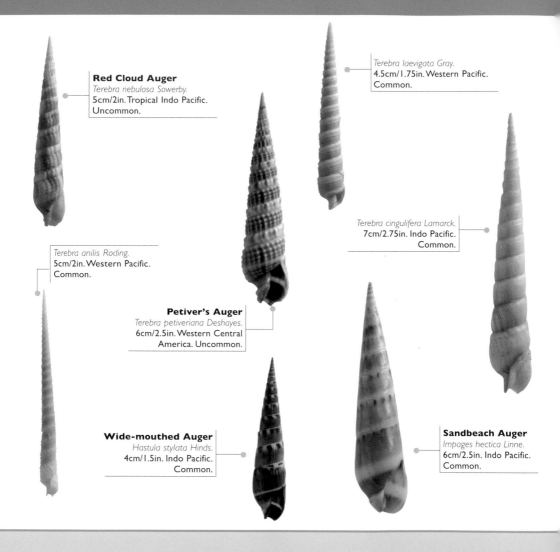

Red Cloud Auger
Terebra nebulosa Sowerby.
5cm/2in. Tropical Indo Pacific.
Uncommon.

Terebra laevigata Gray.
4.5cm/1.75in. Western Pacific.
Common.

Terebra anilis Roding.
5cm/2in. Western Pacific.
Common.

Terebra cingulifera Lamarck.
7cm/2.75in. Indo Pacific.
Common.

Petiver's Auger
Terebra petiveriana Deshayes.
6cm/2.5in. Western Central
America. Uncommon.

Wide-mouthed Auger
Hastula stylata Hinds.
4cm/1.5in. Indo Pacific.
Common.

Sandbeach Auger
Impages hectica Linne.
6cm/2.5in. Indo Pacific.
Common.

SUNDIAL SHELLS

The Architectonicidae is a small family of flat, rounded shells with horny operculae which inhabit varying water depths of warm seas. Some can be difficult to identify due to similarity to other Sundial species.

Clear Sundial
Architectonica perspectiva Linne.
5.5cm/2.25in. Indo Pacific.
Common.

Noble Sundial
Architectonica nobilis Roding.
5cm/2in. Caribbean, Western
Central America & West Africa.
Common.

Giant Sundial
Architectonica maxima Philippi.
6cm/2.5in. Indo Pacific.
Common.

Sharp-edged Sundial
Discotectonica acutissima Sowerby.
4cm/1.5in. Japan to
Northern Australia.
Rare.

Smooth Sundial
Architectonica laevigata Lamarck.
4cm/1.5in. Indian Ocean.
Uncommon.

Straw Sundial
Heliacus stramineus Gmelin.
3cm/1.25in. Indo Pacific.
Uncommon.

Radial Sundial
Philippa radiata Roding.
2cm/0.75in. Indian Ocean &
Western Pacific. Uncommon.

Partridge Sundial
Architectonica perdix Hinds.
3cm/1.25in. Indian Ocean &
Western Pacific.
Uncommon.

Variegated Sundial
Heliacus variegatus Gmelin.
2cm/0.75in. Indian Ocean
& Western Pacific. Common.

BUBBLE SHELLS

Bubble Shells are in the subclass Opisthobranchia. These are generally shell-less molluscs, like sea hares and slugs, but the families Acteonidae and Hydatinidae have shells and some are shown here. They are small to medium, lightweight shells with a wide distribution.

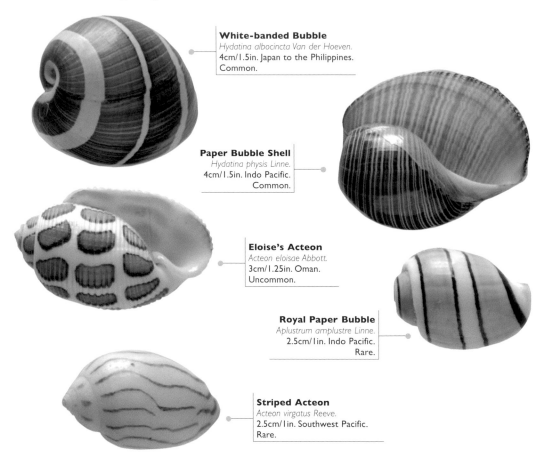

White-banded Bubble
Hydatina albocincta Van der Hoeven.
4cm/1.5in. Japan to the Philippines.
Common.

Paper Bubble Shell
Hydatina physis Linne.
4cm/1.5in. Indo Pacific.
Common.

Eloise's Acteon
Acteon eloisae Abbott.
3cm/1.25in. Oman.
Uncommon.

Royal Paper Bubble
Aplustrum amplustre Linne.
2.5cm/1in. Indo Pacific.
Rare.

Striped Acteon
Acteon virgatus Reeve.
2.5cm/1in. Southwest Pacific.
Rare.

BUBBLE SHELLS

These Bubble shells are in the families Bullidae and Hamineidae.

Atys cylindricus Helbling.
2.5cm/1in. Indo Pacific.
Common.

Common Atlantic Bubble
Bulla striata Bruguiere.
3cm/1.25in. Florida to Brazil & Mediterranean.
Common.

Mabille's Bubble
Bulla mabillei Locard.
4cm/1.5in. Canary Islands.
Uncommon.

White Pacific Atys
Atys naucum Linne.
4cm/1.5in. Indo Pacific.
Common.

Bulla quoyi Gray.
5cm/2in. Australia.
Uncommon.

ark shells

A family of about 200 species, the Arcidae and Cuculaeidae mostly live in warm seas. Solid, heavy Bivalves, they have long, straight hinges with rows of precisely interlocking teeth (toxodant). They live in cracks in cliffs, or on rocks attached by means of a strong thread, called a byssus. Live shells are covered by a thick periostracum. Not popular with collectors.

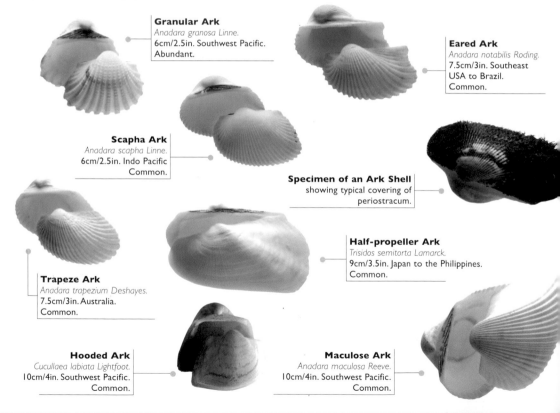

Granular Ark
Anadara granosa Linne.
6cm/2.5in. Southwest Pacific.
Abundant.

Eared Ark
Anadara notabilis Roding.
7.5cm/3in. Southeast
USA to Brazil.
Common.

Scapha Ark
Anadara scapha Linne.
6cm/2.5in. Indo Pacific
Common.

Specimen of an Ark Shell
showing typical covering of
periostracum.

Trapeze Ark
Anadara trapezium Deshayes.
7.5cm/3in. Australia.
Common.

Half-propeller Ark
Trisidos semitorta Lamarck.
9cm/3.5in. Japan to the Philippines.
Common.

Hooded Ark
Cucullaea labiata Lightfoot.
10cm/4in. Southwest Pacific.
Common.

Maculose Ark
Anadara maculosa Reeve.
10cm/4in. Southwest Pacific.
Common.

BITTERSWEET CLAMS

The Glycimerididae are rounded, thickened heavy shells with toxodant teeth similar to those of the Ark Shells. There are at least 100 species living generally in shallow warm seas of the Indo Pacific. They all have a thick periostracum; many are edible.

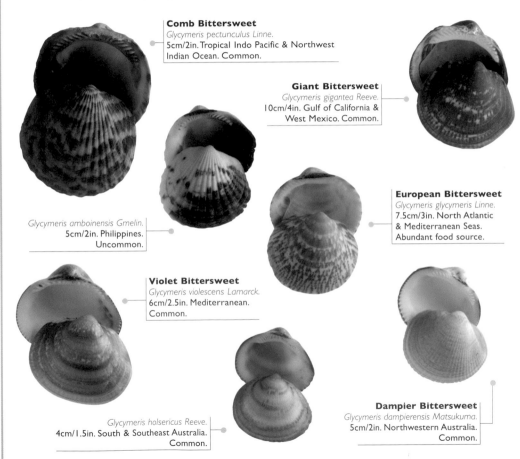

Comb Bittersweet
Glycymeris pectunculus Linne.
5cm/2in. Tropical Indo Pacific & Northwest Indian Ocean. Common.

Giant Bittersweet
Glycymeris gigantea Reeve.
10cm/4in. Gulf of California & West Mexico. Common.

Glycymeris amboinensis Gmelin.
5cm/2in. Philippines. Uncommon.

European Bittersweet
Glycymeris glycymeris Linne.
7.5cm/3in. North Atlantic & Mediterranean Seas. Abundant food source.

Violet Bittersweet
Glycymeris violescens Lamarck.
6cm/2.5in. Mediterranean. Common.

Glycymeris holsericus Reeve.
4cm/1.5in. South & Southeast Australia. Common.

Dampier Bittersweet
Glycymeris dampierensis Matsukuma.
5cm/2in. Northwestern Australia. Common.

189

MUSSEL SHELLS

A well-known group of edible shells, the Mytilidae are widespread in shallow inter-tidal waters where they live in large colonies often attached to rocks by means of their byssus. Most shells are thin and elongate; many interiors are nacreous.

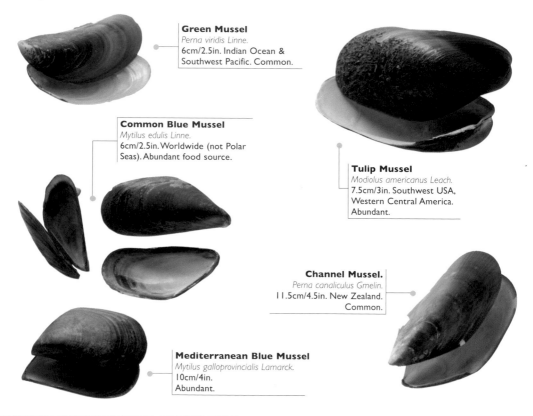

Green Mussel
Perna viridis Linne.
6cm/2.5in. Indian Ocean &
Southwest Pacific. Common.

Common Blue Mussel
Mytilus edulis Linne.
6cm/2.5in. Worldwide (not Polar
Seas). Abundant food source.

Tulip Mussel
Modiolus americanus Leach.
7.5cm/3in. Southwest USA,
Western Central America.
Abundant.

Channel Mussel.
Perna canaliculus Gmelin.
11.5cm/4.5in. New Zealand.
Common.

Mediterranean Blue Mussel
Mytilus galloprovincialis Lamarck.
10cm/4in.
Abundant.

PEARL AND WING OYSTERS

A large family, the Pteriidae live in tropical seas. They all have a highly nacreous interior, and, as in the Black- and Gold-lipped Oyster, grow large and thick to provide vast quantities of nacre for the mother-of-pearl trade. Many are capable of producing pearls, and numerous species are farmed for the pearl industry.

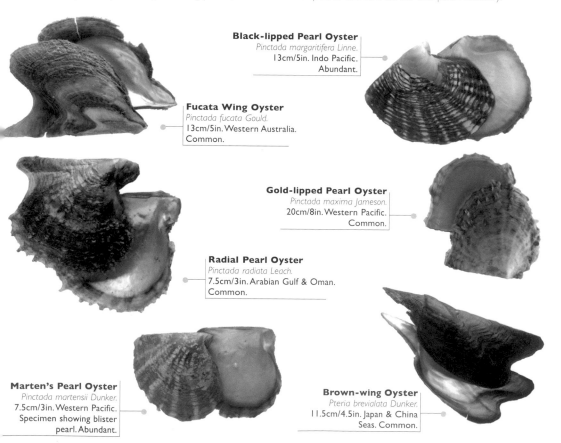

Black-lipped Pearl Oyster
Pinctada margaritifera Linne.
13cm/5in. Indo Pacific.
Abundant.

Fucata Wing Oyster
Pinctada fucata Gould.
13cm/5in. Western Australia.
Common.

Gold-lipped Pearl Oyster
Pinctada maxima Jameson.
20cm/8in. Western Pacific.
Common.

Radial Pearl Oyster
Pinctada radiata Leach.
7.5cm/3in. Arabian Gulf & Oman.
Common.

Marten's Pearl Oyster
Pinctada martensii Dunker.
7.5cm/3in. Western Pacific.
Specimen showing blister
pearl. Abundant.

Brown-wing Oyster
Pteria brevialata Dunker.
11.5cm/4.5in. Japan & China
Seas. Common.

HAMMER OYSTERS

The Malleidae are a strange family of Bivalves with a hammer-like appearance. All have

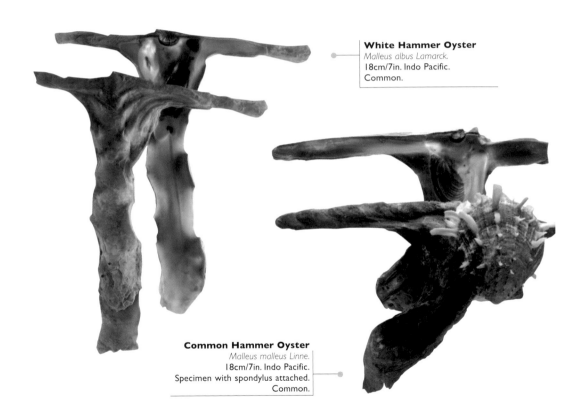

White Hammer Oyster
Malleus albus Lamarck.
18cm/7in. Indo Pacific.
Common.

Common Hammer Oyster
Malleus malleus Linne.
18cm/7in. Indo Pacific.
Specimen with spondylus attached.
Common.

PEN SHELLS

A small family of thin, fan-like shells, the Pinnidae inhabit calm, warm seas, living vertically with their narrow ends buried in sand or mud, and their byssus anchored to stable objects such as rocks. The thin silk-like thread of the byssus was once woven into fine material known as 'cloth of gold'. Some museums exhibit gloves and stockings woven with this very fine substance.

Black Pen Shell
Atrina vexillum Born.
30cm/12in. Indo Pacific.
Common.

Two-colour Pen Shell
Pinna bicolor Gmelin.
35.5cm/14in Indo Pacific.
Common.

FILE CLAMS

Limidae, the File Clam family, are a largish group of Bivalves with coarse, file-like spines covering the exterior shells. They are highly mobile, free-swimming shells, moving with the aid of long tentacles.

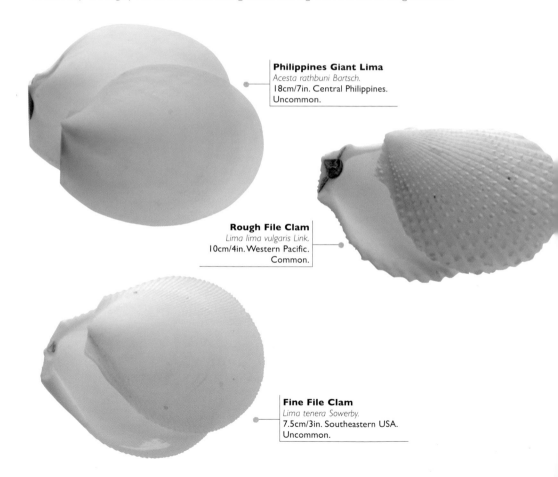

Philippines Giant Lima
Acesta rathbuni Bartsch.
18cm/7in. Central Philippines.
Uncommon.

Rough File Clam
Lima lima vulgaris Link.
10cm/4in. Western Pacific.
Common.

Fine File Clam
Lima tenera Sowerby.
7.5cm/3in. Southeastern USA.
Uncommon.

TRUE OYSTERS

These are a major worldwide food source. The Ostreidae are generally unattractive, varying both in shape and form. The interior is porcellaneous. The Cock's Comb lives in large colonies often amongst mangroves.

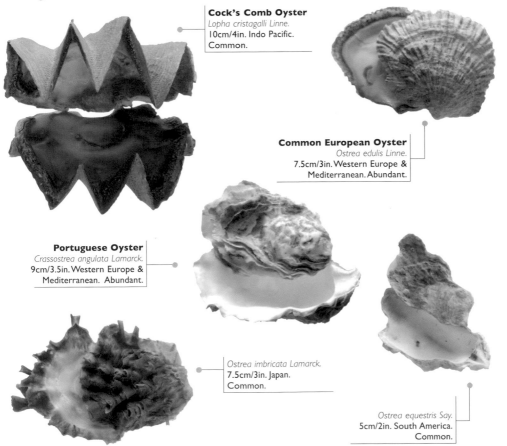

Cock's Comb Oyster
Lopha cristagalli Linne.
10cm/4in. Indo Pacific.
Common.

Common European Oyster
Ostrea edulis Linne.
7.5cm/3in. Western Europe &
Mediterranean. Abundant.

Portuguese Oyster
Crassostrea angulata Lamarck.
9cm/3.5in. Western Europe &
Mediterranean. Abundant.

Ostrea imbricata Lamarck.
7.5cm/3in. Japan.
Common.

Ostrea equestris Say.
5cm/2in. South America.
Common.

AMERICAN SCALLOP SHELLS

Scallops, or Pectinidae, are a very large family of several hundred species of mostly colourful and attractive shells that are very popular with collectors.

They are free-swimming and move by flapping their valves together, butterfly-like.

The shells can be smooth, ridged, or scaly, but all have the characteristic and well-known fan shape. Most species are edible.

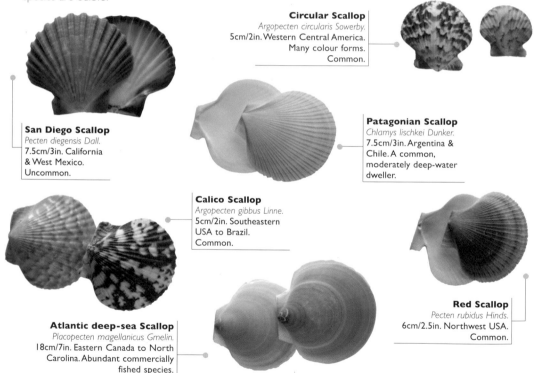

Circular Scallop
Argopecten circularis Sowerby.
5cm/2in. Western Central America.
Many colour forms.
Common.

San Diego Scallop
Pecten diegensis Dall.
7.5cm/3in. California
& West Mexico.
Uncommon.

Patagonian Scallop
Chlamys lischkei Dunker.
7.5cm/3in. Argentina &
Chile. A common,
moderately deep-water
dweller.

Calico Scallop
Argopecten gibbus Linne.
5cm/2in. Southeastern
USA to Brazil.
Common.

Red Scallop
Pecten rubidus Hinds.
6cm/2.5in. Northwest USA.
Common.

Atlantic deep-sea Scallop
Placopecten magellanicus Gmelin.
18cm/7in. Eastern Canada to North
Carolina. Abundant commercially
fished species.

AMERICAN SCALLOP SHELLS

Both the Rough American Scallop and Chlamys sentis occur in a variety of beautiful colours.

Tumbez Scallop
Aequipecten tumbezensis Orbigny.
5cm/2in. Western Central America.
Uncommon.

Palmer's Scallop
Aequipecten palmeri Dall.
4cm/1.5in. Gulf of California.
Uncommon.

Wavy-lined Scallop
Aequipecten lineolaris Lamarck.
5cm/2in. Florida & Caribbean.
An uncommon deep-water shell.

Rough American Scallop
Aequipecten muscosus Wood.
3cm/1.25in. Southeastern
USA to Brazil.
Common.

Chlamys sentis Reeve.
4cm/1.5in. Southeastern USA
to Brazil. Many colours.
Common.

SCALLOPS OF THE NORTH ATLANTIC

The Distorted Scallop is somewhat drab in appearance when compared to the other more colourful species of this region.

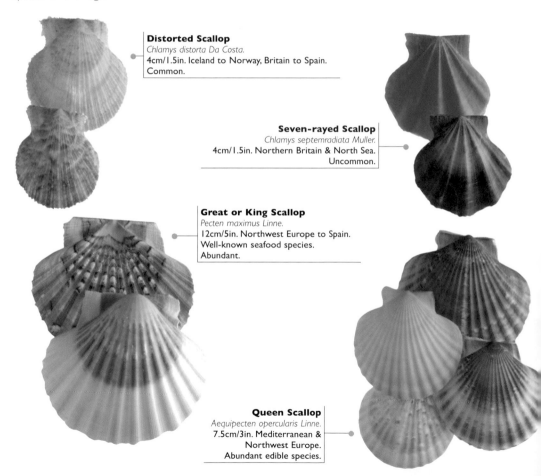

Distorted Scallop
Chlamys distorta Da Costa.
4cm/1.5in. Iceland to Norway, Britain to Spain.
Common.

Seven-rayed Scallop
Chlamys septemradiata Muller.
4cm/1.5in. Northern Britain & North Sea.
Uncommon.

Great or King Scallop
Pecten maximus Linne.
12cm/5in. Northwest Europe to Spain.
Well-known seafood species.
Abundant.

Queen Scallop
Aequipecten opercularis Linne.
7.5cm/3in. Mediterranean &
Northwest Europe.
Abundant edible species.

SCALLOPS OF THE NORTH ATLANTIC AND THE MEDITERRANEAN SEA

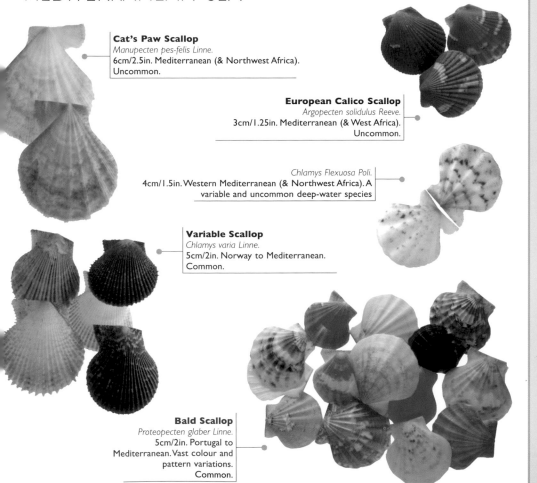

Cat's Paw Scallop
Manupecten pes-felis Linne.
6cm/2.5in. Mediterranean (& Northwest Africa).
Uncommon.

European Calico Scallop
Argopecten solidulus Reeve.
3cm/1.25in. Mediterranean (& West Africa).
Uncommon.

Chlamys Flexuosa Poli.
4cm/1.5in. Western Mediterranean (& Northwest Africa). A
variable and uncommon deep-water species

Variable Scallop
Chlamys varia Linne.
5cm/2in. Norway to Mediterranean.
Common.

Bald Scallop
Proteopecten glaber Linne.
5cm/2in. Portugal to
Mediterranean. Vast colour and
pattern variations.
Common.

COMMON INDO-PACIFIC SCALLOPS

The Senatorial and Noble Scallops occur in a vast range of colours and hues and are popular collector's shells.

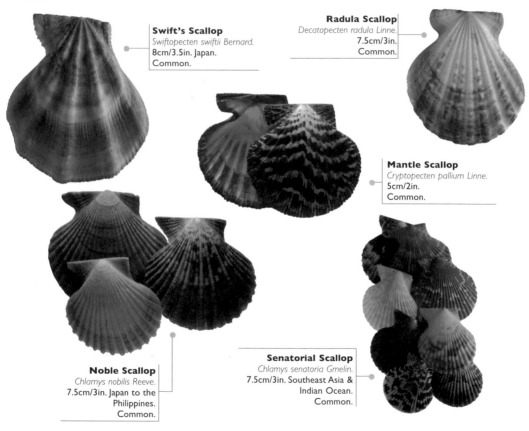

Swift's Scallop
Swiftopecten swiftii Bernard.
8cm/3.5in. Japan.
Common.

Radula Scallop
Decatopecten radula Linne.
7.5cm/3in.
Common.

Mantle Scallop
Cryptopecten pallium Linne.
5cm/2in.
Common.

Noble Scallop
Chlamys nobilis Reeve.
7.5cm/3in. Japan to the
Philippines.
Common.

Senatorial Scallop
Chlamys senatoria Gmelin.
7.5cm/3in. Southeast Asia &
Indian Ocean.
Common.

INDO-PACIFIC SCALLOPS

The Superb Scallop is a beautiful and choice collector's item.

Blistered Scallop
Cryptopecten vesiculosus Dunker.
4cm/1.5in. Japan. Deep water.
Uncommon.

Bractechlamys vexillum Reeve.
4cm/1.5in. Western Pacific.
Common.

Plicate Scallop
Decatopecten plica Linne.
4cm/1.5in. Japan & Western Pacific.
Common.

Superb Scallop
Anguipecten superbus Sowerby.
6cm/2.5in. Southwest Pacific & Japan.
Uncommon.

Scaly Pacific Scallop
Chlamys squamata Gmelin.
7.5cm/3in. Japan & Western Pacific.
Uncommon.

SCALLOPS OF AUSTRALIA AND NEW ZEALAND

Again, many of these species occur in a wide range of colours and are obviously appealing to collectors and shell fanciers alike.

Equichlamys bifrons Lamarck.
7.5cm/3in. South Australia & Tasmania.
Common.

Pecten celator Finlay.
4cm/1.5in. New Zealand.
Uncommon.

Convex Scallop
Mesopeplum convexum Quoy & Gaimard.
4cm/1.5in New Zealand. Uncommon.

Delicate Scallop
Chlamys delicatula Hutton.
5cm/2in. New Zealand.
Variably coloured.
Common.

Mesopeplum anguineum Finlay.
4cm/1.5in. Southern & Southwestern Australia.
Uncommon.

Prickly Scallop
Chalmys asperrima Lamarck.
7.5cm/3in. South Australia & Tasmania. Many colours.
Common.

Dieffenbach's Scallop
Chlamys dieffenbachi Reeve.
4cm/1.5in. New Zealand.
Many colours.
Common.

Pecten atkinos Petterd.
4cm/1.5in. Western Australia.
Uncommon.

SCALLOPS FROM VARIOUS LOCALITIES

Cook's Scallop
*Chlamys cookei Dall,
Bartsch & Rehder.*
5cm/2in. Hawaii.
Uncommon.

Exotic Scallop
Pecten exoticus Dillwyn.
4cm/1.5in. West Africa.
Uncommon.

Chlamys albidus Dall. in Arnold.
7.5cm/3in. Russia to Japan.
Uncommon.

Siboga Glass Scallop
*Propeamusium sibogai Dautzenburg
& Bavay.*
5cm/2in. Japan & Philippines.
Uncommon deep-water species.

African Fan Scallop
*Argopecten flabellum
Gmelin.*
4cm/1.5in. West Africa.
Common.

Yesso Scallop
Patinopecten yessoensis Jay.
22cm/7in. Northern Japan.
Common.

st. james's scallop

During the Middle Ages, Pecten jacobaeus Linne. (found in the Mediterranean Sea and the Canary Islands) became an emblem of Pilgrims travelling to the walled city of Santiago de Compostella, Spain.

The apostle James travelled to Spain to spread the Gospel and establish a small Christian community there. After his death, his bones were brought to Spain by his disciples, where they were buried. Lost for many years, the grave-site and bones were discovered in AD808. A shrine was built, and later the city grew up around it.

James became the patron saint of Spain, and Compostella, next to Jerusalem and Rome, became the third most popular pilgrimage site. Annually, from about the 12th century, thousands of pilgrims travelled by foot or ship to the site.

A legend grew that the ship transporting the bones of St James passed a marriage procession along the shore of Spain. The bridegroom's horse panicked and rushed into the sea. Both rider and horse surfaced unharmed and dry and covered in Scallop shells.

Locals decided to sell Scallops to the pilgrims as souvenirs and in time they became proof of having made the often long and arduous journey to Santiago de Compostela. They were usually attached to hats or cloaks and were considered protection for the journey.

In the 12th and 13th centuries, the Scallop also became a symbol of the Crusaders who fought in the Holy Land. The Scallop was added to the participant's coats of arms.

THORNY OYSTERS

A beautiful family, the Spondylidae are closely related to Scallops. They are highly spinose and colourful Bivalves that live permanently attached to corals and rocks. The shells are frequently covered with marine encrustations, sponge and algae and are difficult to clean. They are occasionally known as 'Chrysanthemum Shells' due to their flower-like appearance. They all possess a unique ball-and-socket hinge structure rather like the human elbow joint.

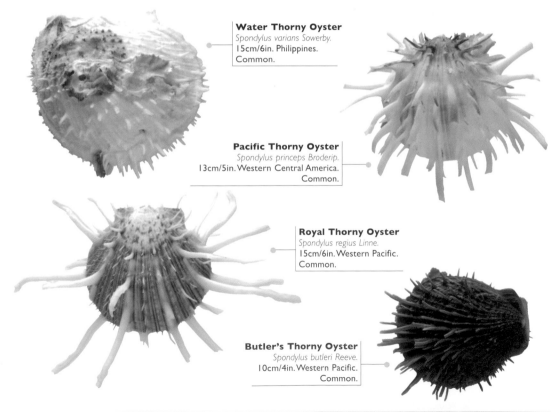

Water Thorny Oyster
Spondylus varians Sowerby.
15cm/6in. Philippines.
Common.

Pacific Thorny Oyster
Spondylus princeps Broderip.
13cm/5in. Western Central America.
Common.

Royal Thorny Oyster
Spondylus regius Linne.
15cm/6in. Western Pacific.
Common.

Butler's Thorny Oyster
Spondylus butleri Reeve.
10cm/4in. Western Pacific.
Common.

JINGLE SHELLS AND WINDOW-PANE OYSTERS

Jingle Shells (Anomiidae) live in colonies, attached to other molluscs and rocks; the smaller lower valve has a unique hole through which its foot and byssus protrude. Worldwide distribution.

The Window-Pane Oysters (Placunidae) are a small group of very thin, flat often translucent shells. They inhabit shallow warm waters. The species shown was used in past times for small window panes. It is now widely farmed in the Philippines for the shellcraft industry.

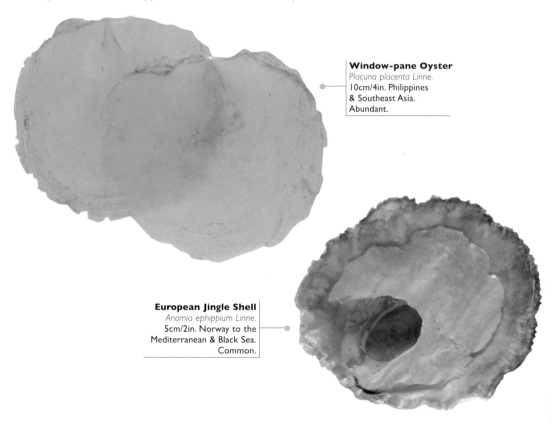

Window-pane Oyster
Placuna placenta Linne.
10cm/4in. Philippines
& Southeast Asia.
Abundant.

European Jingle Shell
Anomia ephippium Linne.
5cm/2in. Norway to the
Mediterranean & Black Sea.
Common.

BROOCH CLAMS

An ancient family, the Trigoniidae have many fossil forms. Now only one genus survives with possibly only two known species, which are restricted to Southeastern Australia.

This species lives in relatively deep water (about 50 metres/164 feet) and has a complex hinge structure. The shells are often used in the jewellery industry due to their highly attractive, nacreous interior.

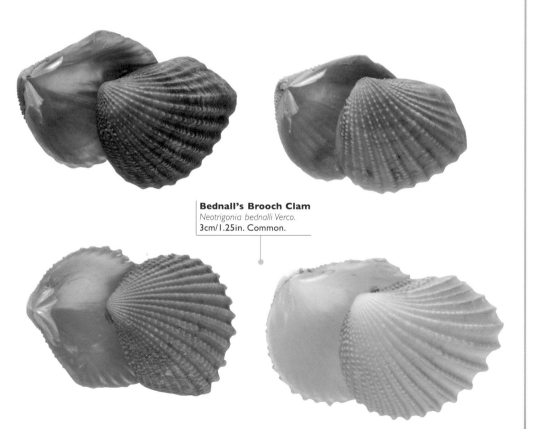

Bednall's Brooch Clam
Neotrigonia bednalli Verco.
3cm/1.25in. Common.

LUCINA CLAMS AND BASKET LUCINES

Lucinidae, the Lucina Clams, are a large family of thick, solid shells that inhabit both shallow and deep water in worldwide locations. Fimbriidae, Basket Lucines are a small family of sand and mud burrowing shells found in warm tropical seas.

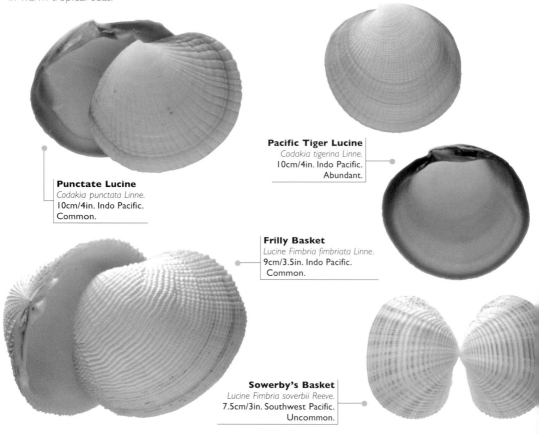

Pacific Tiger Lucine
Codakia tigerina Linne.
10cm/4in. Indo Pacific.
Abundant.

Punctate Lucine
Codakia punctata Linne.
10cm/4in. Indo Pacific.
Common.

Frilly Basket
Lucine Fimbria fimbriata Linne.
9cm/3.5in. Indo Pacific.
Common.

Sowerby's Basket
Lucine Fimbria soverbii Reeve.
7.5cm/3in. Southwest Pacific.
Uncommon.

CARDITA CLAMS

The Carditidae are a fairly large group of thick, strongly ribbed shells found in shallow waters worldwide. They are covered with a periostracum and some produce a byssus.

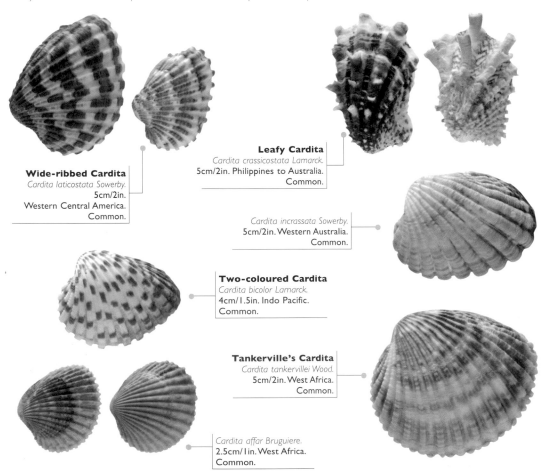

Leafy Cardita
Cardita crassicostata Lamarck.
5cm/2in. Philippines to Australia.
Common.

Wide-ribbed Cardita
Cardita laticostata Sowerby.
5cm/2in.
Western Central America.
Common.

Cardita incrassata Sowerby.
5cm/2in. Western Australia.
Common.

Two-coloured Cardita
Cardita bicolor Lamarck.
4cm/1.5in. Indo Pacific.
Common.

Tankerville's Cardita
Cardita tankervillei Wood.
5cm/2in. West Africa.
Common.

Cardita affar Bruguiere.
2.5cm/1in. West Africa.
Common.

JEWEL BOXES

A small family, the Chamidae are often variable in form and are usually highly coloured and attractive shells. They inhabit warm tropical seas in shallow water where they are attached to rocks or corals. They resemble, in part, the Thorny Oysters.

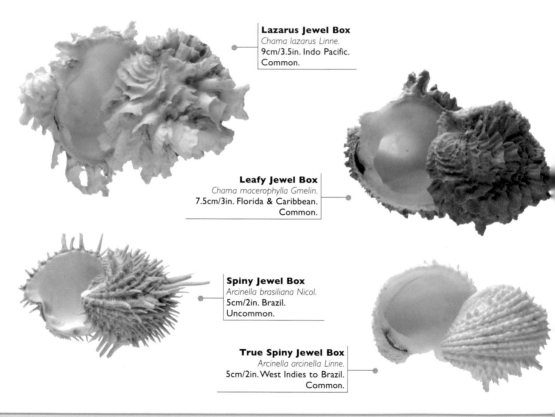

Lazarus Jewel Box
Chama lazarus Linne.
9cm/3.5in. Indo Pacific.
Common.

Leafy Jewel Box
Chama macerophylla Gmelin.
7.5cm/3in. Florida & Caribbean.
Common.

Spiny Jewel Box
Arcinella brasiliana Nicol.
5cm/2in. Brazil.
Uncommon.

True Spiny Jewel Box
Arcinella arcinella Linne.
5cm/2in. West Indies to Brazil.
Common.

COCKLE SHELLS

A large and famous family, the Cardiidae are variable in shape and sculpturing. They can be scaly, spinose, ridged or smooth. Most are edible. Here is a selection of well-known larger species.

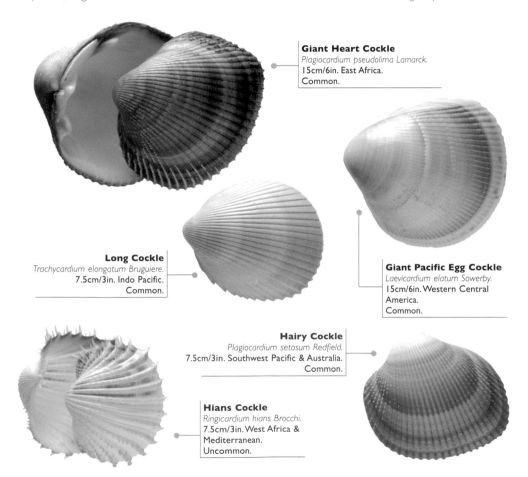

Giant Heart Cockle
Plagiocardium pseudolima Lamarck.
15cm/6in. East Africa.
Common.

Long Cockle
Trachycardium elongatum Bruguiere.
7.5cm/3in. Indo Pacific.
Common.

Giant Pacific Egg Cockle
Laevicardium elatum Sowerby.
15cm/6in. Western Central
America.
Common.

Hairy Cockle
Plagiocardium setosum Redfield.
7.5cm/3in. Southwest Pacific & Australia.
Common.

Hians Cockle
Ringicardium hians Brocchi.
7.5cm/3in. West Africa &
Mediterranean.
Uncommon.

HEART COCKLES

Being mostly heart-shaped, these Cockles are aptly named. Both the True Heart and the Pacific Half-heart Cockle differ from other species in that they appear to open 'sideways'. It is thought that this may be a defence against predatory starfish who perhaps endeavour to force open their valves as they do with other Bivalves!

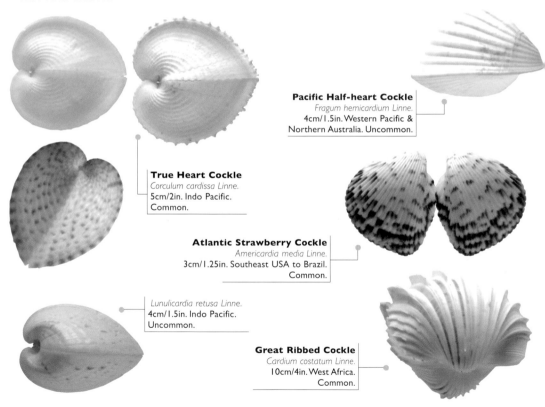

Pacific Half-heart Cockle
Fragum hemicardium Linne.
4cm/1.5in. Western Pacific &
Northern Australia. Uncommon.

True Heart Cockle
Corculum cardissa Linne.
5cm/2in. Indo Pacific.
Common.

Atlantic Strawberry Cockle
Americardia media Linne.
3cm/1.25in. Southeast USA to Brazil.
Common.

Lunulicardia retusa Linne.
4cm/1.5in. Indo Pacific.
Uncommon.

Great Ribbed Cockle
Cardium costatum Linne.
10cm/4in. West Africa.
Common.

COCKLES OF THE MEDITERRANEAN AND ATLANTIC SEAS

The Common European Cockle is an important and long-standing food source. The empty shells are gathered by the tonne and used in the fertilizer industry.

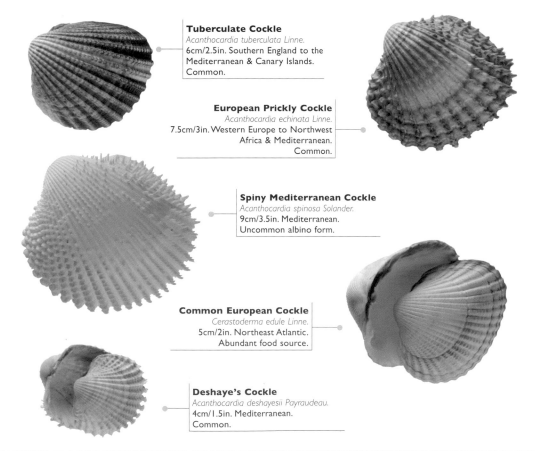

Tuberculate Cockle
Acanthocardia tuberculata Linne.
6cm/2.5in. Southern England to the
Mediterranean & Canary Islands.
Common.

European Prickly Cockle
Acanthocardia echinata Linne.
7.5cm/3in. Western Europe to Northwest
Africa & Mediterranean.
Common.

Spiny Mediterranean Cockle
Acanthocardia spinosa Solander.
9cm/3.5in. Mediterranean.
Uncommon albino form.

Common European Cockle
Cerastoderma edule Linne.
5cm/2in. Northeast Atlantic.
Abundant food source.

Deshaye's Cockle
Acanthocardia deshayesii Payraudeau.
4cm/1.5in. Mediterranean.
Common.

COCKLE SHELLS

The periostracum of the Maroon Cockle is a deep red. When removed it reveals a white-cream shell.

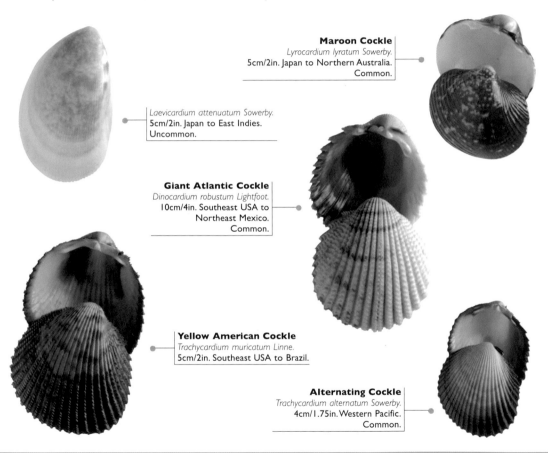

Maroon Cockle
Lyrocardium lyratum Sowerby.
5cm/2in. Japan to Northern Australia.
Common.

Laevicardium attenuatum Sowerby.
5cm/2in. Japan to East Indies.
Uncommon.

Giant Atlantic Cockle
Dinocardium robustum Lightfoot.
10cm/4in. Southeast USA to
Northeast Mexico.
Common.

Yellow American Cockle
Trachycardium muricatum Linne.
5cm/2in. Southeast USA to Brazil.

Alternating Cockle
Trachycardium alternatum Sowerby.
4cm/1.75in. Western Pacific.
Common.

GIANT CLAMS

Most of these clams, the Tridacnidae, have been abundant for centuries, but due to indiscriminate over-fishing, the stocks are severely depleted in many locations in the Indo-Pacific region. No Giant Clams species can be exported from the Philippines, and the CITES (Convention on International Trade in Endangered Species) laws prohibit importation into countries party to the Convention.

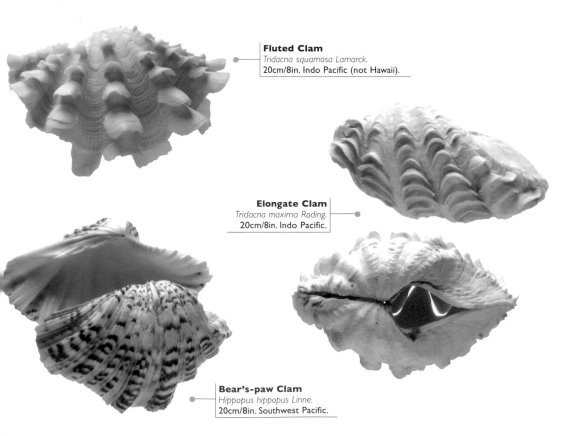

Fluted Clam
Tridacna squamosa Lamarck.
20cm/8in. Indo Pacific (not Hawaii).

Elongate Clam
Tridacna maxima Roding.
20cm/8in. Indo Pacific.

Bear's-paw Clam
Hippopus hippopus Linne.
20cm/8in. Southwest Pacific.

the giant clam

The largest of all seashells, Tridacna gigas is a slow growing monster, often attaining a length of 1.2 metres (4 feet), and weighing in excess of 230 kg (500 lbs).

The Giant Clam lives in warm, tropical Indo-Pacific waters, most commonly in the Philippines where it lives a sedentary life buried in rocks or corals, hinge down. The gaping aperture faces the sunlight, which encourages algal growth, on which the shell feeds. The Giant Clam is an important seafood source and its shells have been used as children's baths, wash basins, church fonts and in general decor.

It is popularly believed that divers have had their limbs trapped within the shell's large aperture. However, no authentication has been recorded. The edges are sharp, however, and care has to be taken when handling these huge valves. Some non-precious porcellaneous pearls can occur in this species.

Few large shells exist in private collections; most can be seen in museums and scientific institutions.

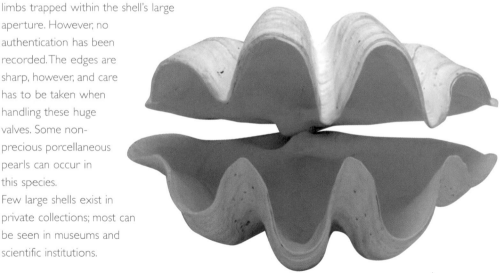

RAZOR CLAMS

Razor Shells (Solenidae) and Jack-knife Clams (Cultellidae) number less than 100 species. They are all narrow, long thin-walled Bivalves with a worldwide distribution. They burrow in sand or mud in shallow waters. Many are edible.

European Razor Clam
Solen marginatus Montagu.
13cm/5in. Western Europe,
Mediterranean & West Africa.
Common.

Ensis arcuatus Jeffreys.
15cm/6in. Norway to Spain & Great Britain.
Common.

Pacific Razor Clam
Siliqua patula Dixon.
13cm/5in. Western coast of
North America.
Common edible species.

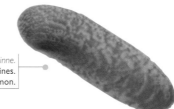

Narrow Jack-knife Clam
Ensis ensis Linne.
10cm/4in. Norway to the Mediterranean.
Common.

Phaxas cultellus Linne.
7.5cm/3in. Japan to the Philippines.
Common.

Sunset Razor
Siliqua radiata Linne.
7.5cm/3in. Indian Ocean.
Common.

TELLIN SHELLS

There are over 200 species of Tellinidae. They are usually small to medium, thin oval shells that have worldwide distribution, living in mud or sand. Most are smooth and shiny with delicate colouration.

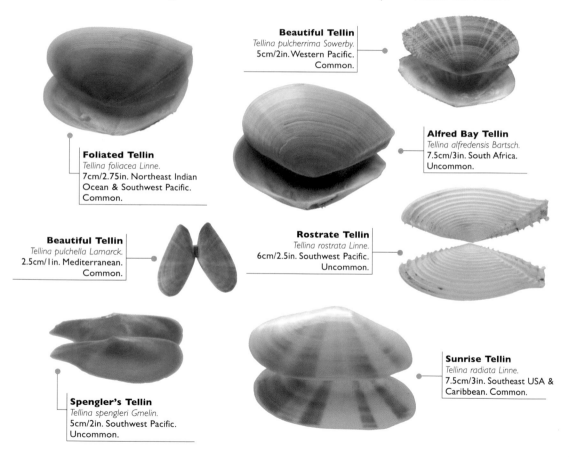

Beautiful Tellin
Tellina pulcherrima Sowerby.
5cm/2in. Western Pacific.
Common.

Foliated Tellin
Tellina foliacea Linne.
7cm/2.75in. Northeast Indian
Ocean & Southwest Pacific.
Common.

Alfred Bay Tellin
Tellina alfredensis Bartsch.
7.5cm/3in. South Africa.
Uncommon.

Beautiful Tellin
Tellina pulchella Lamarck.
2.5cm/1in. Mediterranean.
Common.

Rostrate Tellin
Tellina rostrata Linne.
6cm/2.5in. Southwest Pacific.
Uncommon.

Sunrise Tellin
Tellina radiata Linne.
7.5cm/3in. Southeast USA &
Caribbean. Common.

Spengler's Tellin
Tellina spengleri Gmelin.
5cm/2in. Southwest Pacific.
Uncommon.

WEDGE CLAMS

Donacidae number some 50 or so species and inhabit shallow sand near the inter-tidal zone of most warm and temperate seas. Many are edible, the Coquina Donax is used widely in soup preparation.

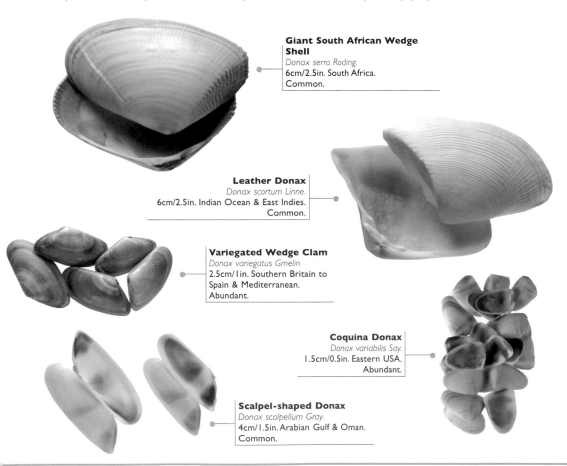

Giant South African Wedge Shell
Donax serra Roding.
6cm/2.5in. South Africa.
Common.

Leather Donax
Donax scortum Linne.
6cm/2.5in. Indian Ocean & East Indies.
Common.

Variegated Wedge Clam
Donax variegatus Gmelin
2.5cm/1in. Southern Britain to
Spain & Mediterranean.
Abundant.

Coquina Donax
Donax variabilis Say.
1.5cm/0.5in. Eastern USA.
Abundant.

Scalpel-shaped Donax
Donax scalpellum Gray.
4cm/1.5in. Arabian Gulf & Oman.
Common.

ARCTICA AND HEART CLAMS

The Ocean Quahog belongs to the small Arcticidae family. There are many fossil forms of this group. Glossidae, or Heart Clams, also belong to a larger fossil group with few existing species. They inhabit both cool and warmer seas and are popular with collectors due to their interesting shape.

Ocean Quahog
Arctica islandica Linne.
10cm/4in. North Atlantic & North Sea.
Abundant.

Moltke's Heart Clam
Meiocardia moltkiana Spengler.
4cm/1.5in. Western Pacific.
Uncommon.

Oxheart Clam
Glossus humanus Linne.
9cm/3.5in. Iceland,
Norway to the Mediterranean.
Common.

VENUS CLAMS

A very large family of varied Bivalves, the Veneridae number in excess of 400 species and inhabit many locations in both warm and cold waters. They live in soft substrates, generally preferring shallow waters. Popular with collectors. Here is a selection of the larger species.

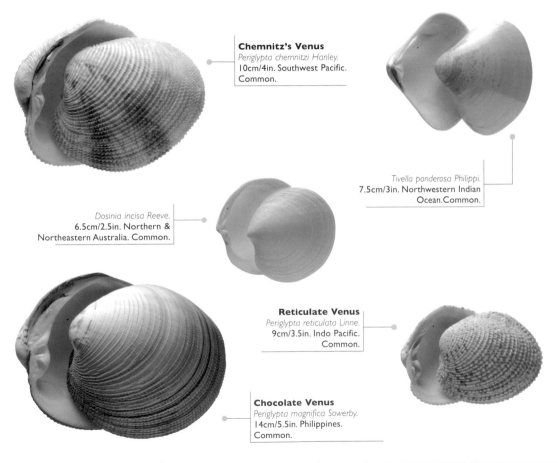

Chemnitz's Venus
Periglypta chemnitzi Hanley.
10cm/4in. Southwest Pacific.
Common.

Tivella ponderosa Philippi.
7.5cm/3in. Northwestern Indian
Ocean.Common.

Dosinia incisa Reeve.
6.5cm/2.5in. Northern &
Northeastern Australia. Common.

Reticulate Venus
Periglypta reticulata Linne.
9cm/3.5in. Indo Pacific.
Common.

Chocolate Venus
Periglypta magnifica Sowerby.
14cm/5.5in. Philippines.
Common.

VENUS CLAMS

The frilly Wedding Cake Venus is well named, resembling delicate icing or fine meringue. A popular collector's species.

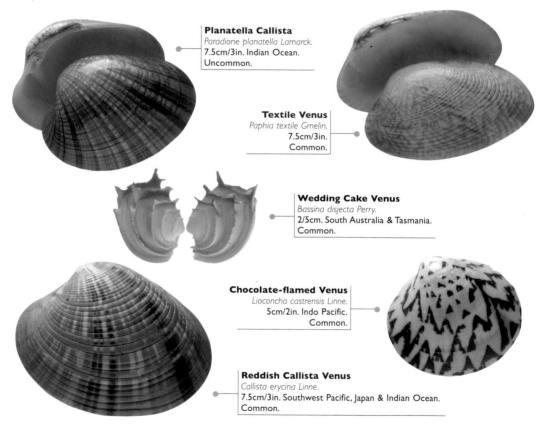

Planatella Callista
Paradione planatella Lamarck.
7.5cm/3in. Indian Ocean.
Uncommon.

Textile Venus
Paphia textile Gmelin.
7.5cm/3in.
Common.

Wedding Cake Venus
Bassina disjecta Perry.
2/5cm. South Australia & Tasmania.
Common.

Chocolate-flamed Venus
Lioconcha castrensis Linne.
5cm/2in. Indo Pacific.
Common.

Reddish Callista Venus
Callista erycina Linne.
7.5cm/3in. Southwest Pacific, Japan & Indian Ocean.
Common.

VENUS CLAMS OF THE NORTH ATLANTIC AND MEDITERRANEAN

Many Mediterranean Venus Clams are used in classic national dishes like Paella and in seafood pasta.

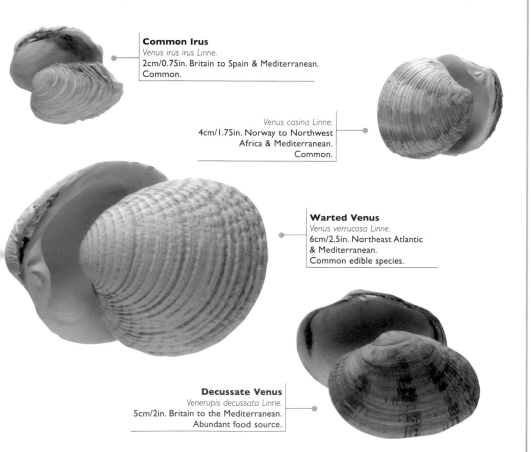

Common Irus
Venus irus irus Linne.
2cm/0.75in. Britain to Spain & Mediterranean.
Common.

Venus casina Linne.
4cm/1.75in. Norway to Northwest
Africa & Mediterranean.
Common.

Warted Venus
Venus verrucosa Linne.
6cm/2.5in. Northeast Atlantic
& Mediterranean.
Common edible species.

Decussate Venus
Venerupis decussata Linne.
5cm/2in. Britain to the Mediterranean.
Abundant food source.

AMERICAN AND CARIBBEAN VENUS CLAMS

Several of the North American clams are used in local seafood dishes. The Pismo Clam is thick and heavy. The Royal Comb Venus has always been a sought-after collector's shell, but perfect specimens are very scarce.

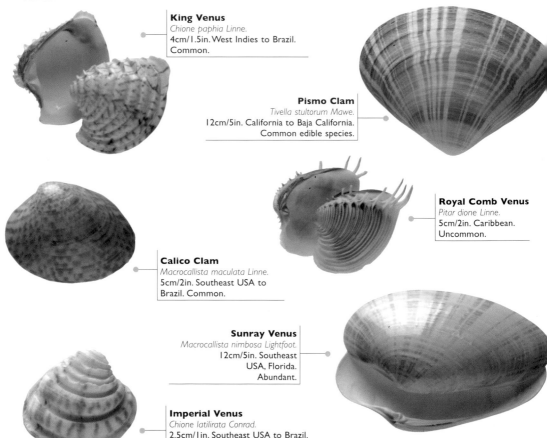

King Venus
Chione paphia Linne.
4cm/1.5in. West Indies to Brazil.
Common.

Pismo Clam
Tivella stultorum Mawe.
12cm/5in. California to Baja California.
Common edible species.

Royal Comb Venus
Pitar dione Linne.
5cm/2in. Caribbean.
Uncommon.

Calico Clam
Macrocallista maculata Linne.
5cm/2in. Southeast USA to
Brazil. Common.

Sunray Venus
Macrocallista nimbosa Lightfoot.
12cm/5in. Southeast
USA, Florida.
Abundant.

Imperial Venus
Chione latilirata Conrad.
2.5cm/1in. Southeast USA to Brazil.
Common.

VENUS CLAMS OF SOUTH AMERICA

Tierra del Fuego Venus
Humilaria exalbida Dillwyn.
9cm/3.5in. Brazil to Argentina.
Uncommon.

Lightning Venus
Pitar fulminatus Menke.
4cm/1.5in. Southeast USA to Brazil.
Common.

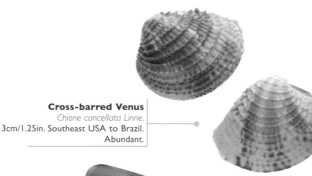

Partially rough Venus
Anomalocardia subrugosa Wood.
4cm/1.5in. Western
Central America. Abundant.

Cross-barred Venus
Chione cancellata Linne.
3cm/1.25in. Southeast USA to Brazil.
Abundant.

Chione intapurpurea Conrad.
5cm/2in. Caribbean to Brazil.
Common.

Trigonal Tivella
Tivella mactroides Born.
3cm/1.25in. Caribbean to Brazil.
Common.

VENUS CLAMS OF SOUTH AMERICA

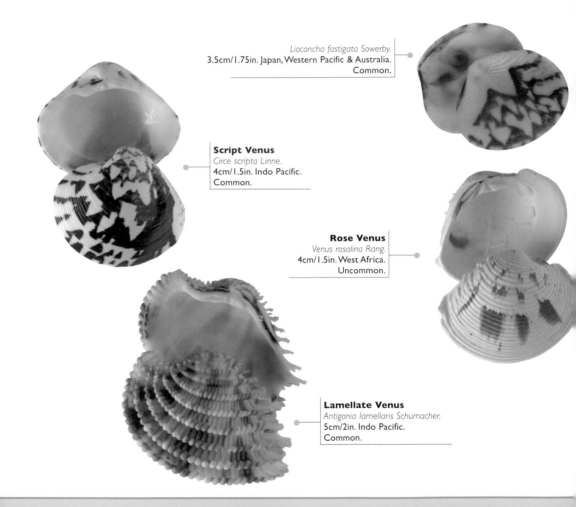

Lioconcha fastigata Sowerby.
3.5cm/1.75in. Japan, Western Pacific & Australia.
Common.

Script Venus
Circe scripta Linne.
4cm/1.5in. Indo Pacific.
Common.

Rose Venus
Venus rosalina Rang.
4cm/1.5in. West Africa.
Uncommon.

Lamellate Venus
Antigonia lamellaris Schumacher.
5cm/2in. Indo Pacific.
Common.

PIDDOCKS, WATERING-POT AND VERTICORD CLAMS

Piddocks, or Pholadidae, live in all seas and are capable of boring into coral, rocks, soft limestone or mud.
The Watering-pots, or Clavagellidae, are like worm tubes, which commence as a Bivalve pair but quickly develop into long tubes as they grow and burrow into sand where they live.
The Rostrate Euciroa is a member of the Verticordiidae family. They are a curious group of rare deep-water species with nacreous interiors.

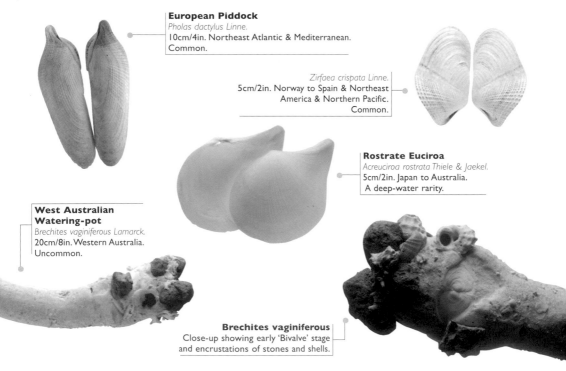

European Piddock
Pholas dactylus Linne.
10cm/4in. Northeast Atlantic & Mediterranean.
Common.

Zirfaea crispata Linne.
5cm/2in. Norway to Spain & Northeast
America & Northern Pacific.
Common.

Rostrate Euciroa
Acreuciroa rostrata Thiele & Jaekel.
5cm/2in. Japan to Australia.
A deep-water rarity.

**West Australian
Watering-pot**
Brechites vaginiferous Lamarck.
20cm/8in. Western Australia.
Uncommon.

Brechites vaginiferous
Close-up showing early 'Bivalve' stage
and encrustations of stones and shells.

chiton shells

The classification of these strange, plated shells is complex and numbers in excess of 600 species. They all inhabit rocky shorelines and night-feed on algae. They are difficult to preserve flat and are often tightly coiled; patterns and sizes vary according to species and are problematic in many cases to identify.

Giant South African Chiton
Dinoplax gigas Gmelin.
10cm/4in. South Africa.
Common.

Giant South African Chiton
Dinoplax gigas Gmelin
(segmented girdle removed.

Callistochiton palmulatus Pilsbryi.
5cm/2in. California.
Common.

Mottled Red Chiton
Tonicella marmorea Fabricius.
2.5cm/1in. Arctic Seas to New
England, Europe & Western Canada.
Common.

Amaurochiton glaucus Gray.
5cm/2in. Australia & New Zealand.
Common.

nautilus shells and spirula

The famous Nautilus Shells (Nautilidae) are a unique group of free-swimming molluscs numbering only five species. They inhabit warm tropical waters on the steep faces of coral reefs where they drop away into deep water. They rest during daytime at about 300–400 metres (984–1,312 feet) before rising to shallower water when dark falls to forage for their prey, mainly crabs.

The octopus-like animal occupies the last, largest chamber of its shell. The shell is large and coiled and closely resembles the fossil ammonites – also Cephalopods, in shape and form. (See The Biology of Seashells p 11-12 for more information.)

Spirula (family Spirulidae) is related to Nautilus and consists of only one species. It has a fragile, loosely coiled shell, which is situated within the rear body of a small deep-sea squid. The shell usually occurs after storms, washed up in many hundreds on beaches, quite commonly, in South Africa and New Zealand. A species that has been widely used in craft work as decoration, in particular in Sailor's Valentines (see Shellcraft p234) .

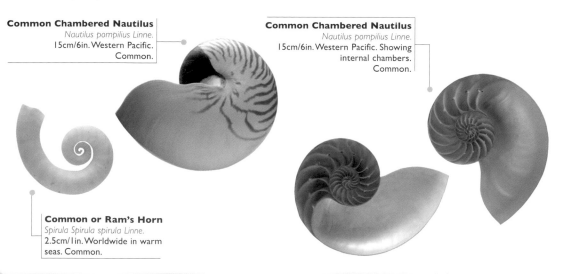

Common Chambered Nautilus
Nautilus pompilius Linne.
15cm/6in. Western Pacific.
Common.

Common Chambered Nautilus
Nautilus pompilius Linne.
15cm/6in. Western Pacific. Showing internal chambers.
Common.

Common or Ram's Horn
Spirula Spirula spirula Linne.
2.5cm/1in. Worldwide in warm seas. Common.

PAPER NAUTILUS SHELLS

The Argonautidae, or Argonauts, are a small family of less than a dozen species. These 'shells' are in fact egg cases of the shell-less Argonaut, and are produced by the female as a receptacle in which to lay her eggs. They are often washed up on shores but are seldom found perfect being paper thin. Large specimens are prized collector's items.

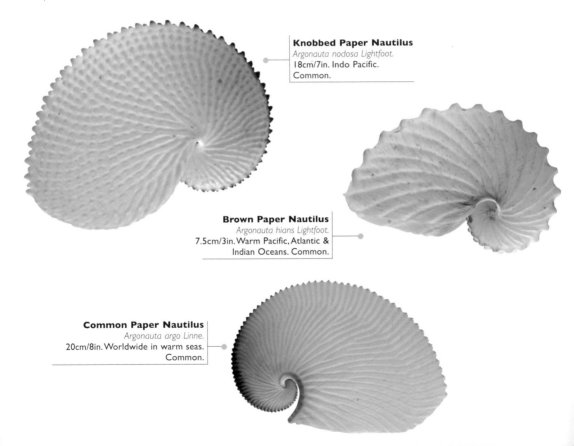

Knobbed Paper Nautilus
Argonauta nodosa Lightfoot.
18cm/7in. Indo Pacific.
Common.

Brown Paper Nautilus
Argonauta hians Lightfoot.
7.5cm/3in. Warm Pacific, Atlantic &
Indian Oceans. Common.

Common Paper Nautilus
Argonauta argo Linne.
20cm/8in. Worldwide in warm seas.
Common.

tusk or tooth shells

The Dentaliidae are a large group of over 1,000 species. They enjoy worldwide locations inhabiting both shallow and deep waters where they burrow in sand or mud with their posterior ends exposed. They vary little in shape; the species differ in pattern, colour, surface sculpturing and size. They are all carnivorous, feeding on foraminifera, protozoans and other micro-organisms. In some species there exists a posterial notch or slit, or a small terminal 'pipe'.

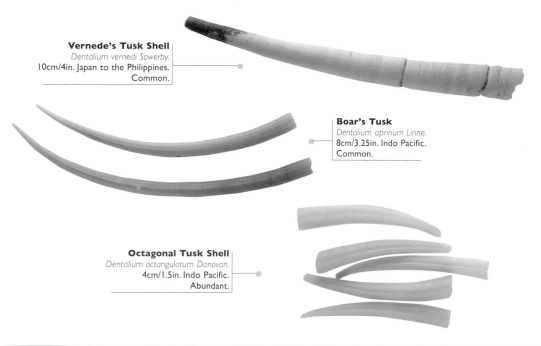

Vernede's Tusk Shell
Dentalium vernedi Sowerby.
10cm/4in. Japan to the Philippines.
Common.

Boar's Tusk
Dentalium aprinum Linne.
8cm/3.25in. Indo Pacific.
Common.

Octagonal Tusk Shell
Dentalium octangulatum Donovan.
4cm/1.5in. Indo Pacific.
Abundant.

SHELL FREAKS AND ABNORMALITIES

As with all living creatures, molluscs can develop abnormalities and freakish variations. The reasons are many; some may be genetic, other can be caused by pollution, upheaval in lifestyle, disease and damage by predators. Molluscs, however, have an amazing aptitude to 'heal' damage, and many shells can be seen with growth scars (particularly Cones) – healed chips or breaks in the outer shell, where the animal has grown new shell on or around the break and continued as usual in its development.

Malformation rarely occurs in Bivalves. In Gastropods, many families and species are prone to unusual variants. Some shells are unnaturally sinistral, left-handed or reversed coiling, and these are often rare and much sought after by collectors. Some Abalones have been found with double rows of perforations, while many Cowries develop twisted and dented shells, some with pronounced extremities.

In New Caledonia, where there is much chemical and mineral presence in the water, due to mining waste being discharged into the sea, numerous Cowrie species develop what is termed 'rostrate' forms, with the ends extended and sometimes upwardly twisted (a possible result of the polluted water). Some species are unusually 'black' or very dark (melanistic) in colouring, and these are known as 'niger' forms.

Species with spines occasionally grow too few or too many, others occur with spines fused together, as in some examples of Spider Conch. All variations from the norm are of interest to the collector and some extreme examples can fetch high prices.

Above: *A species of Rock Shell totally covered with coral*

Above: *A melanistic or 'niger' form of Eglantine Cowrie, Cypraea eglantina from New Caledonia.*

THE SHELL 'DOOR' – THE OPERCULUM

In many Gastropods, never in Bivalves, the snail grows a plate-like structure on its foot, which serves to close off the shell when the animal retreats into its shell. It is described as being either 'horny' or calcareous in make up. The shape usually corresponds to the outline of the shell's aperture. In some species of Conch, the operculum is pointed or claw-like and can be used as a weapon – as in the Florida Fighting Conch.

Although of interest, in particular when trying to identify a species, they are of limited importance to collectors except that the presence with the shell of its operculum usually means that it was live-collected.

SEASHELL CURIOS, JEWELLERY AND SOUVENIRS

Regardless of how exquisite seashells are in their natural state, we have always found ways in which to use, 'beautify' and craft them. The numbers of objects made and ornamented with shells in every culture throughout history are many, and even today shells are very much in vogue in decor, ornamentation and fashion jewellery, as well as being appealing to the collector.

We find shells sold as containers for food and flowers, for bathroom use, or made into a large number of decor items like mobiles and chandeliers (Window-pane Oysters from the Philippines). They are also made into a wide range of both costume and designer jewellery and can be found on market stalls and in high-class city shops.

Simple carving or removal of the outer layers of certain mother-of-pearl shells makes popular and attractive curios and souvenirs, although far too many can be distasteful, often ruining a perfectly good shell. Shell shops in seaside towns are full of shell souvenirs and 'commercial' type specimens, and occasionally you may find the odd unusual or collector-quality shell.

The Victorians loved seashells and the seaside, made popular initially by royalty, and many shell curiosities and seaside souvenirs were made to satisfy demand. Nowadays such objects can be found in sales, auctions and antiques shops and are collector's items.

Left: Paua Shell, New Zeland Abalone. The outer encrusted layer has been removed, finely polished and lacquered with tinted blue to give this stunning effect.

Right: A turban amd two Moon Snails showing operculae in position.

Left: A polished South African Turban. The mother-of-pearl layers are revealed, making these very popular souvenir shells.

SHELLCRAFT

Shell-art, better known as shellcraft, is as popular now as it has ever been. Artists among us will cover boxes and caskets with shells, decorate mirror frames and greetings cards, and make superb collages and 'floral arrangements', as well as inspired items for interior decor. Shell grottoes, which became synonymous with the Victorian era, are still being commissioned from garden designers.

Although not necessarily to everyone's taste, we have always made things from seashells. Since ancient times shells have inspired the artistic to create objects of beauty, interest and use. Wonderful European pieces survive to this day from the early Renaissance, 17th to 19th centuries and, in particular, from the Victorians, who loved embellishments of any kind. 'Sailor's Valentines' are very popular and sought-after collector's items. They were made or purchased by sailors while on long voyages to give to their loved ones back home.

High-quality shellcraft is difficult, exacting, and time-consuming work. The best is sold in salerooms, auctions or in high-class galleries for hundreds, even thousands of pounds. In spring 2002, one of the UK's most eminent shell-artists sold his large shell floral arrangement under a glass dome for £7,000!

SHELLS AS CURRENCY

Cowrie shells are relatively easy to collect and (in particular two small abundant species, the Gold-ringed and Money Cowrie – Cypraea annulus and Cypraea moneta) have been used as currency and trading for several thousand years, perhaps as long ago as 2000BC. The Chinese were possibly the first to use them, obtaining large quantities from the western Pacific Islands.

By the 7th or 8th centuries, the Maldive Islands had become the centre for major distribution to places like Bengal, India, another large distribution centre.

The Cowries' use spread to Afghanistan, Persia and to Europe. Arab traders carried millions of them along established trade routes across the Indian Ocean to the north and west coasts of Africa, where they made enormous profits.

Gold-ringed Cowrie,
Cypraea annulus

At one time in Africa, only two cowries would buy a woman, two generations later 2,500 would buy a cow (a quarter of a woman's price) and by the mid 19th century the number of shells needed to buy a young wife was 60,000-100,000; their value was depreciating!

Their use has diminished drastically over the last 100 years or so, although even in recent times in Africa, their value is still appreciated and trading is still carried out, using loose shells or strings of shells

It is said that Columbus or his men may have taken Cowries to the West, but discovered that the native American Indians had their own highly specialized forms of shell currencies in other species of shells, such as some Bivalves and Tusk Shells.

COUNTERFEIT AND 'DOCTORED' SHELLS

Most collectors and shell fanciers will come across 'doctored' specimens and occasionally the odd 'fake' shell. Shells are quite often worked to remedy defects that would otherwise affect their value. Holes and scars are filled with resin, smoothed over and painted and lacquered to hide the blemish; rough or chipped lips and edges are often filed smooth and broken spines are replaced with adhesive.

In the last few decades, perhaps originally due to a shortage of seashell rarities, Philippino shell-craftsmen have taken things a step further. They craft rare species in wood, often in outrageous sizes, embellish spinose species with even more spines (see above) and cover common shells with thin layers of resin, before painting on a new pattern to closely resemble rarer species. The artwork is extremely time-consuming, and is quite spectacular, very often fooling the layman into purchasing such counterfeits!

Money Cowrie,
Cypraea moneta

Victor Dan's
Angaria.
Extra rows of spines have been cleverly added with adhesive to portray an over-spinose - and a would-be very rare - specimen! Philippines.

The beautiful and much admired Precious Wentletrap is probably associated with the most romantic of shell faking. For many years it was a deep-water rarity, costing up to $200 in the late 18th century – a fortune at that time. It was so scarce that it was said that clever Oriental artisans fashioned them from rice-flour paste. Collectors would only discover the counterfeit when they washed the shells and they fell apart!

Regrettably, however, the story has never really been substantiated. The specimen shown below was long considered to have been a genuine fake, owned for many years by a well-known London shell dealer, Frederick Mayer. Although previous owners each had taken a piece of the shell from the lip region to 'test' its authenticity as a fake, it turned out, sadly, to be a real, but somewhat drab shell!

THE INTERNAL STRUCTURE OF THE GASTROPOD

The vast majority of marine gastropods have coiled shells. It is within these coils that the vulnerable soft parts of the snail are both protected and supported.

The science of Gastropod form and growth is both complex and difficult, but the shells are basically tubes coiled about an imaginary axis growing downwards and outwards from its apex from birth. As the snail grows, so the shell coil is enlarged to further accommodate the larger size, and so on.

Each shell forms a mathematically perfect, logarithmic spiral that can be either flat or upright in formation. It can be seen at its purest in the Chambered Nautilus (see Cephalopods p229-230).

When viewed from above shells generally coil in a clockwise (dextral) direction but occasionally species either naturally (or rarely as an abnormality) develop conversely in an anticlockwise direction. These shells are known to be left-handed, or sinistral.

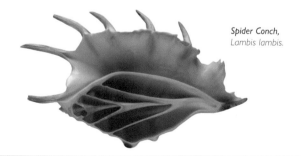

Spider Conch,
Lambis lambis.

THE MOTHER-OF-PEARL TRADE

Not to be confused with 'pearls', mother-of-pearl, or nacre, is a beautiful and unique substance with which many molluscs line their shells. Pearl Oysters, Turbans and Abalones have long provided material for an age-old craft stretching back thousands of years.

The most famous use of the material was for the button industry, reaching its peak in the late 19th century. In ancient times, Oriental craftsmen produced worked and carved pearl plates, which are now very collectable items. In Britain, the mother-of-pearl trade reached a peak in Victorian times, when items such as cutlery handles, calling card cases and decorative boxes proliferated, along with a myriad of jewellery designs. During the 19th century, thousands of tons of the material was shipped from tropical areas to Europe for use in this industry.

Today, many antique traders and restorers use the material (usually in flat pieces) to renovate these much-loved and collectable articles from bygone times.

Victorian mother-of-pearl brooch.

Flat White and 'Gold-lip' mother-of-pearl pieces used for inlay and restoration.
Made in Vietnam.

New Zealnd and American Abalone pieces.
Vietnam.

BIBLIOGRAPHY

As in most specialized subjects, books on shells are not always easy to obtain. Some are highly technical, some are general, basic guides, while others concentrate on one particular family or aspect. Many books are expensive, but they are always a worthwhile investment for the serious conchologist and amateur shell enthusiast.

The ones listed below cover worldwide species, regions of particular interest and large, individual families – which are, of course, invaluable if you decide to specialize. All are highly recommended reading and reference works.

Shells, *S. P. Dance, Dorling Kindersley (UK) 1992*. A very good general guide in the Eyewitness series. Paperback.

Compendium of Seashells, *Abbott & Dance, originally Dutton (N.Y, USA) 1982*. The most comprehensive guide to shells, but small photographs. Hardback.

The Encyclopedia of Shells, *K.R. Wye, originally Headline Books (UK) 1991*. Large colour plates of over 1,000 species. Hardback.

Shells – Treasures of the Sea, *Hill. Hugh Lauter, Levin Inc (USA) 1996*. Excellent large format hardback with emphasis on man's involvement with shells.

Shells of the Philippines, *Leobrera, Carfel Shell Museum (Philippines) 1986*. The only general reference to this popular shelling area. Hardback.

Red Sea Shells, *Sharabati, Routledge & Kegan Paul (UK) 1984*. Very good paperback on this specific area.

European Seashells, *Poope & Goto, Verlag Christa Hemmen (Germany) 1991*. Two volumes on Gastropods & Bivalves. Hardbacks.

Marine Shells of South Africa, *Steyn & Lussi, Ekogilde, CC. (South Africa). 1998*. Hardback.

Australian Marine Shells, *Wilson, Odyssey (Australia) 1994*. Large two-volume work on Gastropods only. Hardback.

Seashells of Eastern Arabia, *Bosch, Dance, Moolenbeek & Oliver, Motivate (UK) 1995*. Fine hardback work.

Guide to Worldwide Cowries, *Lorenz & Hubert, Verlag Christa Hemmen (Germany)*. Major hardback work.

Manual of the Living Conidae, *Rockel, Korn & Kohn, Verlag Christa Hemmen. (Germany) 1995*. First volume of a major work on this subject. Hardback.

Catalogue of Dealers' Prices for Shells, *Rice, Sea & Shore Publications (USA)*.

The author wishes to extend his grateful thanks to the following people who kindly loaned some specimens, photographs and artefacts depicted in this book: Kevin Brown and Alistair Moncur (shell specimens); Mike Fitzgerald (African tribal art); Terry Taylor (Victorian shellcraft); and Tess Morley (modern shellcraft).
CONTACTS: British Museums (in which eminent or notable collections are housed), Natural History Museum, Cromwell Road, London SW7. National Museum of Wales, Cathays Park, Cardiff. The Manchester Museum, The University, Manchester. Royal Scottish Museum, Chambers Street, Edinburgh. The Ulster Museum, Botanic Gardens, Belfast, Northern Ireland. Northants N.H.S. & Field Club, The Humpfrey Rooms, Castilian Terrace, Northampton. CLUBS AND SOCIETIES: The Conchological Society of Great Britain & Ireland (Regular meetings held at the Natural History Museum, London). The British Shell Collector's Club. Hon. Sec. Mr K. Brown, 12 Grainger Rd, Isleworth, Middx. (Meetings bi-annually, held in London). CURRENT JOURNALS & PERIODICALS: Journal of Conchology. Published by the Conchology Society. Pallidula. The magazine of the British Shell Collector's Club. CONSERVATION SOCIETIES: Marine Conservation Society. 9 Gloucester Rd, Ross-on-Wye, Herefordshire.